BIRDS, DISCOVERY AND CONSERVATION

100 years of the
Bulletin of the British Ornithologists' Club

King of Saxony Bird of Paradise (*Pteridophora alberti*), male and female. The species and its nest one hundred years later were first described in the *Bulletin*. Painting by Martin Woodcock.

BIRDS, DISCOVERY AND CONSERVATION

100 years of the *Bulletin of the British Ornithologists' Club*

Edited by
David Snow

HELM INFORMATION

Selection and editorial matter
© 1992 Helm Information Ltd
Helm Information Ltd
The Banks, Mountfield,
Near Robertsbridge, East Sussex TN32 5JY

ISBN 1–873403–15–1

A CIP catalogue record for this book
is available from the British Library.

Frontispiece: King of Saxony Bird
of Paradise
Jacket Illustration: Mikado Pheasant
Both from original paintings
by Martin Woodcock © 1992

Typeset by Leaper & Gard Ltd, Bristol, England
Printed by Hartnolls, Bodmin

Contents

Preface   vii
Acknowledgements   ix
A brief history of the *Bulletin*   1

Geographical ornithology   5

Ornithological exploration at the turn of the century   6
BOU expedition to Dutch New Guinea, 1910–11   13
Expedition to south-western Dutch New Guinea, 1912–13   20
Expedition to Sikkim, 1930–31   22
Expedition to the Sudan, 1939   26

Discovery of the new species and subspecies   31

Mikado Pheasant   31
Ribbon-tailed Astrapia   32
Congo Peacock   34
Irish Coal Tit   36

Migration   39

Report on the first season's work, 1905   39
Massive immigration of northern finches in autumn of 1910   41
Eagle Clarke's 'discovery' of Fair Isle   42
Migration on the Chinese coast   43
Migration at Ushant   44
Influx of continental Jays into southern England   47
The Sooty Falcon *Falco concolor*   50

Ecology and behaviour   57

Goodfellow on the behaviour of birds of paradise   57
Display of snipe and woodcock   61
The evolution of clutch-size   65

The severe winter of 1916–17   68
A severe gale   72
The watering of young sandgrouse   73
Nesting of the Fork-tailed Palm-swift   76
Daily altitudinal movement of the White-collared Pigeon   77

The cuckoo controversy   81

Taxonomy, systematics and evolution   87

Stuart Baker on 'The value of subspecies to the field naturalist'   88
Taxonomy of the Robin   95
A review of some recent researches . . .   105
In defence of the principle of the 'first revisor'   115

The British list   119

First recorded breeding of the Slavonian Grebe in Britain   119
First recorded breeding of the Black-necked Grebe in England   120
British Willow Tit   125
Northern Willow Tit   129
Purple-headed Starlings in the British Isles   130
The Hastings Rarities   134
The Black Woodpecker in Britain   138
Assisted passage   147
Introductions   151

Conservation   153

Protection of the Red Kite   153
Egg-collecting   165
Bird exploitation and conservation at home and abroad   169
    Egret farms in India   172
    The exportation of live birds from Africa   173
    Bird protection in Greenland   175
    Bird casualties on roads   176
Controversial discussion   179

Ornithologists   183
    F.C. Selous   184
    R. Bowdler-Sharpe   185
    P.L. Sclater   189

Appendix   193
Index   195

Preface

When I undertook to edit this ornithological anthology I had some doubts. How could a scientific bird journal with a reputation for publishing sound, useful, but not always exciting, facts and observations relating mainly to bird taxonomy and distribution yield a varied selection of extracts for the interest and, if possible, the entertainment of the ornithological reader? But as I worked through the volumes I found that the subject-matter was surprisingly varied. Its emphasis altered over the years, embracing almost all aspects of ornithology and reflecting the changing interests of ornithologists of past decades. Perhaps this variety was not so surprising after all, as the *Bulletin* published, more or less verbatim, the proceedings of the British Ornithologists' Club, and the Club, for many years after its foundation, was a forum for the most active members of its parent body, the British Ornithologists' Union.

Not all the topics dealt with in the *Bulletin* are, however, suitable for a collection that is designed to be read for enjoyment. Few would get much pleasure from detailed descriptions of new species and subspecies, which constitute a large part of the first fifty volumes. They have become part of the great body of descriptive data now incorporated in standard handbooks. Detailed descriptions of hybrids and of plumage abnormalities, which in some decades featured rather prominently in the pages of the *Bulletin*, are also unsuitable as light reading, as also is the formerly controversial subject of colour change in feathers without a moult, a favourite subject of Dr J.G. Harrison which occupied many pages during his editorship in the 1950s.

The pieces reproduced here for the most part speak for themselves. But the interest of some of them may be enhanced by comment or explanation in the light of subsequent knowledge and developments. With a few exceptions such comment is kept to a minimum. It is given mainly in short introductions to each chapter, or to the sections within the chapters, or, in some cases, comments follow the sections. Some of these are by specialists in the subjects concerned; the rest are by me. The arrangement of chapters is by topics, and the list of topics in itself gives a good idea of the aspects of ornithology that, over the years, were thought to be of greatest interest.

A note on scientific names

In many cases, scientific names of birds used in the early volumes of the *Bulletin* differ from those currently in use. Obsolete names appearing in the following pages, except for those whose identity is clear from the accompanying English name, are identified with current names in an Appendix (p. 193).

Acknowledgements

I take this opportunity of thanking those who have contributed their comments, or helped in other ways: Dr Bruce M. Beehler of the Smithsonian Institution, who directs the Papua New Guinea Program of Wildlife Conservation International and Conservation International, for comments on Goodfellow's accounts of his expeditions to New Guinea and observations of birds of paradise; Dr C.J. Feare, for a comment on the problem of purple-headed starlings; Dr Alan G. Knox, Chairman of the BOU Records Committee, for comments on the British list; Roger Lovegrove, RSPB Representative in Wales, for his comments on conservation of the Red Kite; and J.F. Monk, R.E.F. Peal and Mrs E.F. Warr for drawing my attention to extracts deserving to be quoted or for helping in other ways.

A brief history
of the *Bulletin*

The British Ornithologists' Club was founded at an inaugural meeting in London on 5 October 1892. Its membership was to consist (as it still does) of members of the British Ornithologists' Union, all BOU member who wished being eligible to join for an annual fee of five shillings. Its purpose was to enable members of the BOU to meet more frequently than at the single annual meeting, by holding monthly meetings, from October to June, at which specimens would be exhibited, papers on ornithological subjects read, and discussion invited. As soon as possible after each meeting an abstract of the proceedings was to be printed, distributed *gratis* to members and sold (to non-members wishing to buy it) at a shilling each. Although the rules make no mention of it, the meetings, which were held at a London restaurant or hotel, included a dinner. Thus the Club had both a scientific and a social purpose.

To begin with, and for many years subsequently, the contents of the *Bulletin* consisted, not of papers presented in the form to which we are now accustomed, but of items of various kinds and various lengths, presented in some such form as:

> Mr. SCLATER exhibited a prepared wing and tail of the Martineta Tinamou (*Calodromas elegans*), and pointed out that this form of the Tinamidae had 12 rectrices, although these feathers could not be discriminated from the adjacent coverts without careful examination.

or

> Mr. SEEBOHM next exhibited and made remarks upon a new species of *Zosterops* from East Java, procured by Mr. John Whitehead in 1886, which he proposed to call ZOSTEROPS NEGLECTA, sp. n.

or

> A communication was read from Mr OSBERT SALVIN FRS, on two new species of birds from Nicaragua, as follows:–
> 'In a collection of birds recently sent by Mr. W.B. Richardson from Nicaragua, several interesting species are represented which, so far as I know, have not hitherto been noticed in Nicaragua ...'

The longer papers, usually printed throughout in inverted commas, were nearly all the texts of talks given at a meeting. It was not until Dr Jeffery Harrison took over the editorship of Volume 72, in 1952, that the main contents of the journal consisted, not of summaries of material exhibited and remarks made at a meeting, but of papers submitted for publication in the modern way.

P.L. Sclater, who was the Club's Chairman from its foundation until his death twenty-one years later, opened the second session of the Club in October 1893 with an address, in which he reviewed the notable ornithological events of the past year. The annual Chairman's address became one of the *Bulletin*'s regular features, continued by his successors until it was finally abandoned during the Second World War. Some of the Chairman's addresses are still of considerable interest, and extracts from them are to be found in the following pages. P.L. Sclater's annual address was a hard act to follow, not made any easier for his successor, the Hon. Walter Rothschild, by a shyness which he never managed to overcome. He began as follows:

> Brother Members of the BOC,
> It is a very difficult task at all times to make a beginning; and I find this axiom very true in my own case. To follow in the steps of our late Chairman will be difficult indeed; but to read one's first address is a most terrifying ordeal.

The exhibiting of interesting specimens, especially of new species, remained a major part, in fact to a large extent the *raison d'être*, of the Club's meetings for many years. It had become less frequent in the years preceding the Second World War, ceased during the war, and only happened on rare occasions after the war, the last report in the *Bulletin*, in the old style, being the exhibition by J.M. Harrison of 'six specimens of *Bombycilla garrulus centralasiae* Poljakow, a new British form', on 18 June 1952. Perhaps the crowning exhibit was that produced at the meeting on 12 May 1920, when 'Lord Rothschild exhibited a full-sized model of the Moa *Dinornis maximus* Owen, together with a drawing of Moa feathers and a photograph of a cast of the skeleton in the Royal College of Surgeons'. He had arrived at Pagani's Restaurant with the nine-foot-high model sticking out of the roof of the taxicab.

When the *Bulletin* began, Latin was still recognised as an international language for publications in taxonomy, and some of the descriptions of new birds in the early volumes were in Latin. English soon took over, and no Latin text appears after 1909. The Club evidently had among its members at least one accomplished Latin scholar. When the final volume of the monumental *Catalogue of Birds* was published in 1898, the Club devoted its next volume (Volume IX) to 'An alphabetical index to the genera adopted in the twenty-seven volumes of the Catalogue of the Birds in the British Museum'. To commemorate the occasion, an anonymous member of the Club composed the following verses, which were printed in the preface to the index:

De Catalogi Avium Magni Scriptoribus undecim

Sharpius *incepit, scripsitque volumina multa;*
  Seebohmus *sequitur, promptus ad auxilium.*
Teutonicus, zelo plenus, venit inde Gadovus,
  Salvinus*que bonam praebet amicus opem.*
Jam Sclaterus *adest, tria longa volumina complens,*
  Americanarum notus amans avium.
Expers Hargittus *nunc Picos ordinat omnes,*
  Hartertus*que sagax Cypselidas numerat.*
Multum etiam pensae Shelleyi *profuit ardor,*
  Multum Saundersi *mens operosa dedit.*
Clarus ab Italia jam Salvadorius *adstat,*
  Et tandem Grantus *fine coronat opus.*

[On the eleven authors of the Great Catalogue of Birds
Sharpe began it, and wrote many of the volumes;
Followed by Seebohm, ever ready to help.
Then, full of zeal, comes the German, Gadow;
And our friend, Salvin, lends welcome support.
And now comes Sclater, renowned expert in American birds, and
  writes three long volumes.
Then experienced Hargitt puts all the Pici into order,
And wise Hartert catalogues the swifts.
Shelley tackles his task with great enthusiasm,
And industrious Saunders makes a major contribution.
Now renowned Salvadori from Italy gives his help,
And finally Grant crowns the work.]

As mentioned above, it was Dr J.G. Harrison who in 1952 effected the transition of the *Bulletin* from its original form to that of a conventional ornithological journal. It continued, however, to appear nine times a year, following each of the Club's meetings, a regime which now seems an intolerable strain for an editor. This continued under J.J. Yealland's editorship, but when C.W. Benson took over, in 1969, he reduced the frequency of publication to six issues a year, and in 1973 to four issues, thus completing the *Bulletin*'s transformation to a conventional modern journal. What has not changed has been its small format and modest – not to say old-fashioned – appearance, which is surely appreciated by those who read it in trains and those who bind and keep the row of uniform volumes on their shelves.

Geographical ornithology

'Geographical ornithology' – the discovery of the world's birds and working out of their ranges – was the main interest of most nineteenth-century ornithologists. In his opening address on 22 October 1902, Sclater put it more formally and more elegantly:

> On opening the eleventh session of the British Ornithologists' Club and on the occasion of their nineteenth meeting, I beg leave to say a few words before the ordinary business of the meeting is commenced. In so doing I propose to confine my remarks to the geographical side of ornithology, that being, I think I may say, the branch of our science in which most of us are mainly interested, although, as editor of *The Ibis*, I have always endeavoured to secure contributions relating to every branch of our subject. It was to geographical ornithology – that is, to the study of the birds of the different countries of the whole world – that the minds of the founders of the BOU were principally directed when they founded the Society in 1858, and the meeting at which we are gathered together tonight is, in fact, a selection of the most active members of the Union, who love to run about the world and collect birds in every land.

By the time the *Bulletin* was started, in 1892, a great deal was known, but new discoveries were constantly being made, and Britain, with its empire, was a good base for ornithologists of means (as most were), some of whom employed collectors in distant parts of the world, while others organised their own expeditions. Most favourably situated of all were soldiers, administrators and other professional people stationed in the colonies and other dependent territories.

There has been a tendency to think that nearly all the bird species in the world have been discovered. Ernst Mayr wrote in 1946, 'I doubt that in the entire world as many as 100 new species remain to be discovered' (*Auk* 63: 64–9); but in the event this estimate turned out to be far too low, as detailed exploration of remote areas, and especially isolated tropical mountains, produced a spate of new and often surprising discoveries, summarised in a succession of papers by Mayr and his co-workers (most recently, *J. Orn.* 128 (1987): 137–50). It is interesting that the same mistake was being made much earlier. In his address on opening the Club's third session in 1894, P.L. Sclater said:

More than forty years ago, as I well recollect, my former friend and master in ornithology, Hugh Strickland, used to complain how hard it was to find a bird really new to science. Strickland was little aware of the enormous number of new species and new forms, some of them of the most extraordinary character, which have been constantly discovered and described year by year since that period.

There is little doubt (though exact counts would be time-consuming) that more of these new discoveries have been published in the *Bulletin* than in any other journal.

The two following extracts from Sclater's Chairman's addresses give the flavour of this now remote period of ornithological imperialism. These are followed by notable accounts, based on talks given to the Club, of expeditions to New Guinea, Sikkim, and the Sudan.

Ornithological exploration at the turn of the century

From the Chairman's address, 19 October 1898.

But the brethren of the BOC and their friends, I think I may say, are at present not less active in the field than in the cabinet. We are fortunate in having with us tonight the two principal members of the new expedition to Socotra and Southern Arabia which will leave England on the 28th inst. It will, of course, take up natural history in every branch, but with Dr Forbes and Mr Ogilvie Grant as its leaders, and a trained taxidermist in attendance, we need not fear that the interests of ornithology will in any way be overlooked. In Socotra itself much has been already done, but little or nothing has been ascertained ornithologically of the southern coast of Arabia, and we know, from Bent's writings, that even in this commonly supposed barren district, bird-life is abundant in certain spots, which we trust may be within reach of the expedition.

Besides the Socotran expedition many other explorations by various members of the BOU are in progress or in contemplation. Captain Boyd Alexander, who has worked so well in the Cape Verde Islands, is struggling through the middle of Africa from the Cape to Cairo. Under present circumstances he seems likely to come out successfully, and will, no doubt, bring information on birds, if not specimens, with him. Mr Lort Phillips hopes to return to his favourite quarters in Somali-land during the course of the present winter, and expects to get together the supplementary materials still required for the preparation of his proposed work on the birds of that most interesting country. Mr John Whitehead, who has added so much to our knowledge of the zoology of the Philippines, proposes to return to the same country very shortly, in order to continue his researches in a field which he knows so well and in which he takes such great interest. Before leaving, he has placed in the hands of the editors of *The Ibis* a series of valuable field-notes on the birds collected during his last journey. These will appear in the forthcoming volume of our journal. Mr Alfred Sharpe, CB, who is shortly returning to his post in Nyasaland, promises to continue the employment of collectors in different parts of that protectorate, the zoology of which he, following in the footsteps of Sir Harry Johnston, has already done so much to investigate.

Finally, I may remark that, as will be seen on turning over the pages of contents in the last volume of *The Ibis*, we have correspondents interested in our favourite subject in nearly every part of the world, and that the great difficulty of the Editors is to compress so many valuable contributions within the compass of an annual volume.

Before resuming my seat, I wish to say one more word. Our Government, in connection with that of Egypt, has just taken possession of an enormous district in Africa, probably nearly equal to half Europe in extent. It sternly warns all intruders off, even when they are alleged to be of 'no political influence'. When it comes to regulate the administration of these new territories, it is to be hoped that the interests of natural history will not be entirely overlooked. Although the Upper Nile districts have been traversed and investigated by many well-known naturalists, there is still very much to be done in these teeming regions of animal life. We Englishmen are ready and willing to undertake, by individual efforts, much work that in other countries is provided for by state explorers; but it is not too much to expect that our Government should at least help us by providing adequate facilities and occasional assistance, and even, perhaps, by contributions to the expensive process of bringing the results thus acquired completely before the world.

The chairman's address, 21 November 1900.

Brother Members of the BOC,

On commencing the ninth session of our Club I venture to remind you that we have now issued ten volumes of our *Bulletin*, and have recorded in them a goodly series of ornithological observations and of new discoveries in bird life.

But I may also remind you that our Club is, as it were, a Committee of the British Ornithologists' Union, embracing, as it does, nearly all the most prominent and most active members of the larger Society. The British

Ornithologists' Union has just brought to a close the seventh series of its journal *The Ibis*, making a total of forty-two volumes devoted to the advancement of our favourite branch of natural science. This is therefore, I think, a good opportunity for considering shortly some of the principal results which have been accomplished by the BOU during the forty-two years that *The Ibis* has flourished.

One of the principal objects of those who originally conceived the idea of a British Ornithologists' Union and founded *The Ibis* was that we should use it as a means of publication for the results of our own travels and expeditions into various parts of the world in search of birds and of the incidents of bird life. Thus, the very first volume of our first series contained articles by Salvin on his experiences in Guatemala, by Canon Tristram on the birds of Palestine and also of Algeria, by Prof. Newton on the birds of St Croix, West Indies, and by Evans and Sturge on the birds of Spitsbergen. The original idea of our journal was quickly expanded; we received accounts of the collections made by our friends and correspondents in various parts of the world, and these were worked out mainly by the experts at home. But all through the long series of *The Ibis* the geographical interest remains a prominent feature. One may consult any volume of *The Ibis* and the student will find that most of the principal articles are devoted to the ornithology of some special country or district, and that the field-notes form a special feature. Research such as this we may boast to have carried on in nearly every district of the known world. In the words of the Roman poet we may fairly exclaim:

Quae regio in terris nostri non plena laboris?

One can look through the pages of *The Ibis* and find that the Arctic and Antarctic regions, the tropics, the subtropics, and the temperate climes of both hemispheres have been alike the subject of our investigations. Wherever bird life exists, the British ornithologist seeks to penetrate. He is always on the look-out for untrodden fields to explore.

After forty-two years of this sort of work, in which it must be recollected that our ornithological brethren in Germany, America, and other countries have been by no means slow to rival us, it would perhaps be supposed that there are no more 'worlds left to conquer', and that work on the geographical branch of ornithology will soon come to an end. But such, I believe, is by no means the case, excepting, perhaps, in North America, where our friends across the Atlantic have nearly exhausted this particular branch of the subject. I will endeavour to set before you what I consider to be some of the principal *hiatus valde deflendi* in geographical ornithology, and to express a hope that some of our young and energetic associates may take steps to fill up the gaps in our knowledge.

I The Palaearctic Region

This, as the seat of our original civilisation, is naturally the best known and most completely explored of the six great regions. Of its western division the *Ornis Balcanica* of Reiser has filled up what was until recently one of the least-known portions. Morocco, Algeria, and Tunis have also received a great deal of attention. Egyptian birds are now well known, but a new edition of Capt. Shelley's volume on the birds of that country is much required. The northern portion of the eastern division of the Palaearctic Region is in the hands of the Russian naturalists, and we must lament that the important works commenced by Dr Pleske (*Ornithographia Rossica*) and Professor Menzbier (*Ornithologie du Turkestan*) have remained so long unfinished. The time has also now arrived when a new handbook of the birds of Europe should be undertaken. We are glad to hear that Mr Dresser is busily engaged in preparing a *Manual of Palaearctic Birds*.

In the far east of the Palaearctic Region British ornithologists have done their full share of work. No one can forget the name of Swinhoe when treating of this subject, and we have several active contributors to *The Ibis* (Rickett, Styan, La Touche) always busy on the birds of the Chinese Empire. There is no doubt, however, that great discoveries have still to be made when the mountainous ranges of the interior of China can be safely explored. An enterprising ornithologist who would undertake to go out to Kamtchatka or the Lower Amoor in the early spring and watch the migrants coming north on that side of the globe would find a very interesting field of research. This was a pet scheme of our late friend, Seebohm, and will, we may hope, be taken up some day by one of his followers.

Another vacant area on the boundaries of the Palaearctic Region, which is easy of access and might be safely traversed in the early spring, lies between the Persian Gulf and Palestine. The traveller should proceed to Bussorah by sea, and thence journey up the valley of the Euphrates to Aleppo and Antioch. Not many novelties, perhaps, would be obtained on this route, but, so far as I know, the district has hardly ever been visited by a naturalist, and many interesting species of birds would doubtless be encountered.

II The Indian Region

The extent and variety of the ornis of the Oriental Region are so great that it is impossible to do more than just allude to it on the present occasion. British ornithologists have again done their full share towards the elucidation of its zoological features, and are still doing good work. The excellent *Fauna of British India*, edited by Blanford, with the volumes on *Aves* by Mr Oates and himself, sums up what has been done within the limits of our Indian Empire.

Oustalet's new work on the ornis of the Cochin-Chinese provinces, of which the first part is already issued, will supply much required information on the further side of the continental portion of this region. All the great islands of the Oriental Archipelago have now been more or less investigated, and a splendid volume on the ornithology of the debatable land of Celebes has been lately provided for us by the labours of Dr A.B. Meyer and Mr Wiglesworth. At the same time it must not be supposed that even here there is not much more work to be done by the patient collector. It is difficult to point to the exact locality in the Oriental Region to which the traveller should be specially directed. The sad fate of John Whitehead prevents me from suggesting Hainan with is unhealthy climate, and the Philippines are at present closed to ornithological investigation; but there are many crumbs to be picked up by the student of zoology in the Malayan Archipelago, as Mr Rothschild's collectors have recently shown us.

III The Ethiopian Region

It is in the Ethiopian Region, perhaps, that geographical ornithology has made the greatest progress of late years. In nearly every district, both in the south and along a broad band running up Eastern Africa to Somaliland, collections have been made and described, and vast additions have thus accrued to our knowledge of the African ornis. Among those who have contributed to this result I may mention the names of Alexander, Andersson, Forbes, Ogilvie Grant, Jackson, Johnston, Lord Lovat, Lort Phillips, Bowdler Sharpe, Shelley, and Weld-Blundell as efficient workers in the field or in the cabinet. But there have been many other celebrated collectors, and our German colleagues have been especially active. These extensive acquisitions to our knowledge of the Ethiopian ornis are now being worked up in the two summaries prepared, one in this country by Capt. Shelley and the other at Berlin by Prof. Reichenow. Capt. Shelley in his first volume enumerates more than 2,500 members of the African ornis, but he includes in his work the species of Madagascar and the Mascarene Islands, which do not strictly belong to the Ethiopian Region, in my opinion. There must be, however, still considerable additions to be made to the list. It is difficult to specify the most likely localities for future researches, but the ranges north of Mount Elgon (now easily accessible from Mombasa) and the highlands of our new Protectorate of Nigeria deserve special attention. Moreover, since the days of Rüppell no naturalist has visited the high plateau of the interior of Abyssinia, and there is certainly much to be done in these regions of Africa.

IV The Nearctic Region

Turning now our attention for a few moments to the New World, we may, as already hinted, safely leave the ornis of the Nearctic Region in the care of our good friends in the United States. In the last number of *The Auk* we are informed that the first volume of Mr Ridgway's long-promised work on *The Birds of North and Middle America* will shortly be issued. It will probably run to seven volumes, and will deal with about 3,000 species and subspecies. This is welcome intelligence, as we know that the work will be thorough and exhaustive, even though we may not always agree with the nomenclature employed in its pages.*

V The Neotropical Region

In the *Nomenclator Avium Neotropicalium*, published twenty-eight years ago, upwards of 2,500 species were assigned to the Neotropical Avifauna, and at least 500 more, I should estimate, have been added to it since that period. The Neotropical Region is without doubt the richest in bird life of the six great zoological areas of the globe, and is scarcely surpassed in extraordinary forms by the Papuan Subregion of Australasia. In the division of the Neotropical Region north of Panama we have in the 'Birds' of the *Biologia Centrali-Americana* an excellent account of our knowledge of this Avifauna as far as the *Accipitres*.

All over South America much good work has been done of late years in nearly every part of its wide extent, and a new feature in the scientific history of the continent is the publication in Brazil of important essays on the avifaunas of these countries by Dr von Ihering and Dr Goeldi. In the highlands of Peru and Bolivia, however, although so much has been already done, fresh novelties are sure to be met with in the unvisited valleys; and the eastern frontiers of Colombia and Ecuador still deserve further attention. There is, in fact, much hard work to be accomplished by patient research carried out in nearly every part of this region. To those who may be tempted to take short trips to South America I should recommend a visit to the Sierra de Cordova (easily accessible by rail from Buenos Aires) and to the adjoining ranges to the north. Or a run over the ocean to Pará; but instead of going up the Amazons, it would be better for the ornithologist to search the hill country south of Pará, and hunt up *Pipra opalizans* and other little-known

---

*Sclater never accepted the use of trinomials, which Ridgway was one of the first to use in a major systematic work. Several years later, when the trinomial system was well established and Hellmayr was using it in his great *Catalogue of the Birds of the Americas*, Sclater was again to say: 'I do not by any means approve of Mr Hellmayr's views on nomenclature, but I fully appreciate the value of his work and agree with most of his conclusions.'

species confined to that district, which has never been properly explored. Field-notes on South American birds are still greatly to be desired.

We greatly appreciate, however, the recent additions to the avifauna of Ecuador made by Mr Goodfellow and Dr Festa, the latter having formed the subject of a memoir by our old friend Count Salvadori. The British Museum has also received important collections from Ecuador, Peru, and Bolivia from Mr P.O. Simons, and of these we are promised descriptions shortly by Dr Bowdler Sharpe.

VI The Australian Region

The wealth of bird life in the Australian Region is apparently inexhaustible. Of the avifauna of Australia itself we have indeed a fair knowledge – thanks mainly to the energy of John Gould and his disciples. But in the other subregions there is still a large residue of bird work to be accomplished. It is here that the ambitious ornithologist who does not fear to risk his health should betake himself.

Gould published his *Handbook of Australian Birds* in 1865, and it is now quite time that we should have a new work on the same subject, correcting errors and introducing the species added to the list during the past thirty-five years. We have active workers in Sydney, Melbourne, and elsewhere in Australia, and now that the colonies are united under an imperial governor there will be a fine opportunity to start such an enterprise. We should invite our Australian friends and correspondents to lay their heads together and see how this great work can best be done.

In the Papuan Subregion there is a particularly well-finished piece of work for us to build upon, viz. Count Salvadori's *Ornitologia della Papuasia*, of which the last supplement was issued in 1891. Much has been done since that date, but, as I have just said, much more remains to be accomplished. *Pteridophora alberti*,* in some respects the most wonderful bird in the world, was only discovered in 1894, and who can say that equally or still more remarkable novelties are not to be found in the unexplored interior of New Guinea? Here, indeed, there is a task to be undertaken – difficult, no doubt, but to be accomplished like other difficult tasks, if proper means are employed. New Guinea still remains the country that aspirants for high honours in ornithological science should try to explore.

Finally there remains the Polynesian division of the Australian Region. Of what was known of the feathered inhabitants of this subregion in 1891 we have a capital summary by Mr Wiglesworth in his *Aves Polynesiae*. But every island in Polynesia should be visited and its birds observed and catalogued; this has as yet been by no means effected. Even in the New Hebrides, as

*The King of Saxony Bird of Paradise, described by A.B. Meyer in the *Bulletin* in 1894.

shown by Capt. Farquhar and Dr Bowdler Sharpe in the last volume of *The Ibis*, there are new species to be discovered by a careful search.

The geography of ornithology has always been one of my favourite subjects, and I must ask your pardon for having spoken of it at such length. But if my remarks have the effect of inducing our brethren of the BOC to take up some few of the many points of enquiry that I have set before them, I shall not consider that I have wasted your time.

The King of Saxony Bird of Paradise

For nearly 100 years after its discovery the King of Saxony Bird of Paradise remained little known. Nothing was known of its nesting until 1988, when Clifford and Dawn Frith discovered a nest and made detailed observations which, like the original description, were published in the *Bulletin* (vol. 100 (1990): 160–64). The nest, and single egg, were quite similar to those of other members of the subfamily Paradisaeinae, to which the King of Saxony Bird of Paradise belongs; for the details, which cannot easily be abbreviated or summarised, the reader is referred to the Friths' paper. They set the scene for their account as follows:

The bizarre appearance of the adult-plumaged male King of Saxony Bird of Paradise has attracted great interest ever since its description in 1894, which even the great British Museum ornithologist Bowdler Sharpe thought must have referred to an artifact or hoax specimen. By the time of his monograph on the Paradisaeidae, Sharpe (1898) was, however, convinced of the authenticity of the remarkably plumaged mature male and he stressed the great need for information on the nesting of birds of paradise, especially for forms such as *Pteridophora*. Remarkably this knowledge has eluded numerous expeditionaries, collectors and ornithologists ever since, until now.

At 1030 hr on 24 December 1988 a female-plumaged ... King of Saxony Bird of Paradise was seen carrying a piece of moss in her bill and flying to a nest 10.9 m up in a large tricate upright branch fork of a *Timonius belensis* tree, situated on a gentle slope at an altitude of 2665 m a.s.l., at Tari Gap (5° 57'S, 143° 10'E), Southern Highlands Province, Papua New Guinea ...

BOU Expedition to Dutch New Guinea, 1910–11

Walter Goodfellow's account

Mr Chairman and Gentlemen,
I have been asked to give some account of the birds of the region visited by

the BOU expedition to Dutch New Guinea. My remarks must necessarily be limited, owing to the fact that I was obliged to return home through continuous ill-health, just as we had reached the mountains where the more interesting species were to be met with. Nearly all the rarer birds were collected after I had left the country, and the bulk of the skins still remains to be worked out and many of the species to be identified. The dense impenetrable nature of the country affords the naturalist less opportunity of studying its bird life than any other part of the world that I know of.

What first struck us on landing at the Mimika was the apparent paucity of bird life, and this was also noticeable for a considerable distance from its mouth until the mangrove swamps were passed. When we first landed a number of pelicans, terns, and waders were seen on the low sand-banks which stretch far out to sea, but could not be identified as they admitted of no near approach, and later on practically disappeared from those parts, our arrival having attracted fleets of canoes from all parts of the coast, east and west, which no doubt scared the birds away.

Throughout the mangrove belt, which reached right up to our base-camp at Wakatimi, bird life was very limited. A few white cockatoos (*Cacatua triton*) could generally be seen, but always flew away screaming at our approach. One species of Lory, *Chalcopsittacus scintillatus*, was fairly common, also the Black-and-White Fruit-Pigeon (*Myristicivora spilorrhoa*), which seems to be confined entirely to mangrove swamps, not only here but elsewhere. It was observed breeding in May along the creeks near the mouth of the river, there being no less than seven nests in one tree. Usually a few solitary Black Cockatoos (*Microglossus aterrimus*) might also be seen on the lower river, sitting on the tops of the highest trees. The call of this bird, a loud clear whistle, always attracted attention, and even from their high perches their red faces and erect crests were conspicuous.

Here we also obtained a few specimens of the large Kingfisher (*Dacelo intermedia*), but it was by no means common. Among the riot of parasitic plants which cover the trees a few sunbirds and small honey-eaters might always be seen. The nests of the former suspended from fallen and partially submerged dead trees were continuously swinging from side to side, the strong current in the river keeping the trees in perpetual motion. These nests might easily be mistaken for a handful of drift left there by the river. Probably the most conspicuous bird on the lower river was the Kingfisher (*Sauromarptis gaudichaudi*), and its loud grating call could be heard in all directions. The natives brought numbers of half-fledged young ones to our base-camp during May and June, which were purchased by the Javanese soldiers and convicts. As they gave them boiled rice only, it is needless to say that their lives were very brief. At the base-camp the true jungle commenced, and here birds were more numerous, but, owing to the still denser growth, were more often heard than seen, and unless their calls were known, identification was often impossible. Two or three days after we landed the Gurkhas brought in the first Cassowary. It was impossible to skin it, but I made a careful note of the colours of its soft parts. Since looking at Mr Rothschild's plate of *Casuarius intensus*, I have no hesitation in attributing it to that species. The casque was erect (not turned over as in most of the specimens of *C. sclateri*, of which we subsequently shot many) and finely shaped. The wattles were only partially divided and of a light blue colour with a few pinkish marks on the underside. When I was leaving the country eight months later one of the Gurkhas brought in the head of another specimen identical with the first, but, as far as I know, this species was never met with on the Upper Mimika, whereas *C. sclateri* was common to both parts and fairly numerous. The natives have distinct names for the male and female birds and, judging from the quantities of feathers in their possession, must often succeed in capturing them. Eggs and newly hatched chicks were brought in during January and February. On one occasion at Parimàu some Cassowary's eggs must have been kept by the natives for a few days before they hatched, for young ones were brought to us which had evidently just emerged from the shells. Cassowaries were seen at various times by different members of the expedition searching for food in the pools and shallow waters of the river-beds, and during the cross-country marches they sometimes dashed across our trail, but afforded scarcely a momentary glimpse. In July at Parimàu one was often heard calling during the night quite close to our camp, and, judging by the very large tracks it left in the soft mud, I should say that it was a female. A couple of hours after daybreak on one of the following mornings a male bird was observed on the bank of the river opposite our camp, and within a dozen yards of the village, trying to cross the swollen waters to our side. One of the soldiers fired at it, but with no result. The next morning at the same hour the bird appeared again at the same spot. This time a Gurkha succeeded in wounding it, and after crossing the river and following it up in the jungle, he at length secured it.

Near the base-camp *Goura sclateri* was fairly common, and was met with from thence onwards wherever we went. In spite of the numbers we shot for food during the whole of the time the expedition remained in the country, the supply did not appear to diminish. This pigeon and a few others afforded the only fresh meat we obtained. On the canoe-journeys up the river they were frequently to be met with in the early mornings in twos and threes searching for aquatic life along the muddy banks. When first disturbed by our approach they did not immediately take flight, but with wings raised pirouetted around for a few seconds and then flew to the nearest high tree. I often found the remains of small crabs in their stomachs, and a large percentage of the birds shot were badly infected with a small red parasite, the same or similar to that which is known in other parts of New Guinea as 'scrub itch'. Two young ones taken from the nest had the iris pale greenish-grey, which eventually changed to brown in one which lived in camp for several weeks. The bird was about a month old when it died, but up to that time the iris showed no trace of the ruby-red of the adult bird.

Halcyon sanctus was undoubtedly the most conspicuous bird about our base-camp, where its harsh cry could be heard all through the hot hours of the day. Our houses and storehouses were infested with myriads of black crickets, which, taking the place of cockroaches in other countries, committed fearful havoc among our stores and personal possessions. The constant packing-up of goods to send up the river drove thousands of them to seek fresh shelter in other parts of the camp. At these times the kingfishers became very tame and darted in and out among the buildings, taking advantage of the feast thus afforded. Mr Claude Grant shot here a single specimen of the lovely kingfisher *H. nigrocyanea*, the only one obtained. Other species at the base-camp were *H. macleayi*, *Alcyone lessoni*, and *A. pusilla*.

A few very high trees were left standing near our huts at Wakatimi, and these morning and evening were the resort of such species as *Mino dumonti* and *Calornis metallica*, as well as a few cockatoos and Eclectus Parrots. For a long time during the hot midday hours some bird rested there which possessed a remarkably sweet Thrush-like song, and we were most anxious to catch a glimpse of it. After watching for many days, I found it to be Robertson's Golden Grackle (*Melanopyrrhus robertsoni*). Its song would not have remained unnoticed even in countries where the birds, as a rule, have sweeter voices than those of New Guinea. During part of April and May the Mimika was invaded by a species of fly somewhat resembling our Mayfly, but larger and of a canary-colour. In some places the surface of the water was absolutely yellow with them skimming about. All along the banks many birds were preying upon them – *Merops*, *Eurystomus*, *Rhipidura*, and *M. robertsoni* in flocks. Strange to say, there was also a small kingfisher, *Ceyx solitaria*, representing a genus which I had hitherto thought to be exclusively a fish-eater. After our base-camp had been established for some time, it was visited every evening by a number of nightjars (*Caprimulgus macrurus*), which no doubt found such a large open space an admirable hunting-ground, and their graceful evolutions gave us much pleasure to observe. When long grass had sprung up in the clearing outside the stockade, a small finch (*Munia tristissima*) put in an appearance. Behind the village at the back of the camp lay a swamp which every night was the roosting-place of thousands of lories, chiefly *Eos fuscata*, and there were also smaller flocks of *Trichoglossus cyanogrammus*. Long before sunset and until it was quite dusk flocks of many hundreds coming from all directions flew over with a deafening noise. Often some weak branch would give way under their weight and cause a panic just as the noise was beginning to subside; clouds of them would again circle around seeking a fresh roosting-place and keeping up a continual din. Although *Lorius erythrothorax* and *Chalcopsittacus scintillatus* were also common (especially the latter species) in the same neighbourhood, I never observed them roosting with the other lories.

On those tedious journeys between the base-camp and Parimàu the gloomy banks were occasionally enlivened by a momentary flash of bright colour from some such species as *Todopsis bonapartei* and the little kingfisher *Ceyx solitaria*, previously mentioned. *Merops ornatus* also swarmed in some places after the month of April; previous to that we had not seen any. Small flocks of the pale-coloured crow *Gymnocorax senex* were frequently to be seen, their shrill but weak call always striking one as quite uncrow-like. At some of the stopping-places on the river night was made hideous by the mournful call of the Frogmouth (*Podargus papuensis*), repeated to distraction on every side, and finishing up with a peculiar sharp snap.

The call of *Paradisea novae-guineae* could often be heard on the upper parts of the river, but during many journeys up and down, on a single occasion only did I catch a glimpse of one. On the Wataikwa River in August I collected a number of full-plumaged males and immature birds in all stages of moult, and it would seem as though there is no regular moulting-season. Nowhere where we went could it be said that these birds were plentiful. The Pygmies often brought the plumes of *P. minor* to Parimàu and traded them with the natives there. As we never came across that species, I think there is no doubt that the Charles Louis Range forms its boundary. As the Pygmies live to the west they probably trade with the natives over there. The Rifle-bird (*Ptilorhis intercedens*) was fairly common both on the coast and near the mountains, in fact at Parimàu and Wataikwa its call was heard at almost all hours of the day, and might be mistaken for that of the Black Cockatoo, which it much resembles, consisting of two long-drawn-out notes, one ascending and the other descending. *Parotia meeki* was obtained after I left, as also that most beautiful species, *Xanthomelas ardens*. While watching some pigeons through my glasses on the opposite bank of the river at No. 4 camp, I saw a small bird rise from the top of a tree and soar into the air like a Sky-lark. After it had risen about thirty feet it suddenly appeared to collapse and fell back into the tree as if it had been shot. It was a King Bird-of-Paradise (*Cicinnurus regius*), and probably this was part of its display. Although I watched for a long time, the performance was not repeated.

Along this part of the mountains that curious parrot *Dasyptilus pesqueti* was fairly common. Its hoarse, grating call, quite unlike that of any other parrot with which I am acquainted, could be heard a long way off. The species usually moved about in parties of four or five individuals, and occasionally I saw as many as seven together. When not feeding they always chose the tallest trees to rest in, preferring dead ones which towered above the general level of the jungle, where they would remain for hours at a time in rain or sunshine. They do not climb after the usual manner of parrots, but jump from branch to branch with a jerky movement like the lories, and with a rapid flicking movement of the wings. They feed entirely on soft fruits, chiefly wild figs. Our skins of this species from the Mimika may possibly be found to be a trifle smaller than those from SE New Guinea. From the Wataikwa camp every evening I observed large flocks of *Gymnophaps albertisii*

17

coming from their feeding-grounds in the high mountains to roost in the plains below. Their flight is extremely rapid, and their strange evolutions in the air remind one of 'tumbler' pigeons at home. The Black-and-White Flycatcher (*Malurus alboscapulatus*) was a delightful little bird which frequented the tall grasses in the immediate vicinity of the same camp. It has an undulating flight as it crosses the open from one clump of reeds to the other, and is very tame.

As our expedition was primarily an ornithological one, it is much to be regretted that the last batch of coolies, which I got together and sent from Macassar, was not employed to push on to the Saddle Peak at the back of Parimàu, where it would have been possible to collect up to an altitude of 8,000 to 9,000 feet. Instead of this they were worn out with long marches across country to reach points suitable for survey work only. It had long been known that it was impossible to reach the snows from our base of operations on the Mimika, and the move eastwards should therefore have been abandoned altogether.

No doubt Mr Wollaston is right in believing that Carstensz Top could best be reached from the Oetakwa River, but at the time we commenced operations little was known about that river, and that little was not at all favourable. Those who had been up it for some distance had found no dry land, and I was told by the authorities in Batavia that if we attempted to ascend the Oetakwa a depot ship would be necessary as a base-camp, and that they could not supply. All those who were best acquainted with the coast as far as it was known advised us to try the Mimika.

* * *

Goodfellow is not far wrong when he notes the difficulty of studying birds in New Guinea. And boiled rice is still offered as a staple diet to captive birds by villagers in the Far East. His comments on cassowaries highlight how little we still know concerning the remarkable variation exhibited in coloration of the bare skin of the head and neck. *Goura sclateri* (the Southern Crowned Pigeon) continue to be shot for the stewpot and trapped illegally for the export bird trade that flourishes in eastern Indonesia. Because of these depredations their future may be in jeopardy.

Goodfellow's observation of the aerial flight display of the King Bird of Paradise (*Cicinnurus regius*) has not been repeated, but a similar courtship dance is carried out by Wallace's Standardwing (*Semioptera wallacii*) of the northern Moluccas and has been documented by K. David Bishop.

I feel grateful that I did not have to suffer the hardships weathered by Goodfellow to share some of his wonderful experiences on the largest tropical island on earth.

BRUCE M. BEEHLER

Account by A.F.R. Wollaston, who acted as medical officer,
entomologist, and botanist to the BOU expedition.

Mr Chairman of the BOC, Mr President of the BOU, and Gentlemen,
You have already heard from Mr Goodfellow a good deal about the birds,
and from the cinematograph and lantern-slides you will know about the
natives, pygmies, and others that we met, so I will make a few remarks about
the conditions of travel in southern Dutch New Guinea.

In addition to the physical and climatic disadvantages of the country, you
find yourself confronted with two very serious obstacles. One of these is the
lack of native labour and means of transport in the country itself, which
necessitates importing coolies at immense cost from outside. It is true that we
occasionally employed as carriers some of the natives who lived near the
hills, but they would never go more than three days' journey from their
village: often we had to wait several days before they would condescend to
start at all, and they were not to be depended on in any way.

The coolies that we employed – three batches of about fifty men in each –
came from Amboyna, Banda, and Macassar. Like the majority of the Malay
races, these people were not very strenuous – the average load they carried
was about 30 lbs – and they quickly succumbed to the combined effects of
the climate and of their food, which was necessarily rather rough. We know
now from our own experience and from that of Dr Lorentz that the only
people of the Malay islands who are likely to withstand the hardships of such
an expedition are the Dyaks of Borneo. Our Gurkhas kept in better health
than any others in the expedition, and it would probably be better to take
coolies from Northern India; but this is perhaps a counsel of perfection.

The other great drawback to travelling in this part of New Guinea is the
total lack of food: there are no villages with well-stored granaries to draw
upon, no deer or antelopes to shoot, and no plantations of mealies or
bananas to plunder. You may well ask what the natives in such a country do.
Certainly there are fish in the sea and in the rivers, and in the low-lying
swamps near the coast is any quantity of sago; but it is the first object of an
expedition to the mountains to leave that country behind.

So it follows that every scrap of food for Europeans and coolies alike has to
be imported into the country and carried laboriously wherever the expedition desires to go. When I tell you that a party travelling with Malay coolies
carrying, in addition to food, only the most necessary camp equipment,
exhausts its supplies in fourteen days, you will understand what are the
limitations of this sort of transport. It means that you must progress by
means of depots of food, and the process is a very slow one. For instance,
suppose you wish to establish a depot of food at a place six marches above
your base-camp, the coolies would consume six days' food on the way up
and (if they marched well) three days' food on the way down; thus they would
leave only five days' food at the depot. It requires very little imagination to

understand that it will be a long time before enough provisions can be stored at the first depot in order to begin the establishment of a second depot six marches further on. The task is not an impossible one, but it requires very careful calculation, and it involves a good deal of hardship to even the best of coolies.

Expedition to south-western Dutch New Guinea, 1912–13

From the report on the Club's meeting on 11 June 1913.

Mr A.F.R. Wollaston gave the following account of the expedition to the Utakwa River, SW New Guinea.

Our party consisted of Mr C.B. Kloss, an engineer, five Dyak collectors, and 74 Dyak carriers; the escort, provided by the Dutch Government, numbered 130 men under the command of Lieut. Van de Water. We left Java on the 31st of August in a government steamer and anchored a few miles up the Utakwa River on the 18th of September. In seven days all our baggage had been landed and a base-camp established about twenty miles from the sea. A fortnight later we proceeded up the river in six large canoes, which had been made by the Dyaks. Two days' journey took us as far as it was possible to go by water, and there a second permanent camp (Canoe Camp) was made. Three marches from the river a camp was made in the foothills at an altitude of about 2,500 ft, and collectors were sent there as soon as possible. When sufficient stores had been accumulated at that place a preliminary excursion was made for six marches into the mountains in the middle of December, and at the end of that month two collectors were sent up to a camp between 4,000 and 5,000 ft. In the middle of January we set out on our excursion to the highest mountains, and at the ninth camp from the river (about 6,000 ft) two collectors spent a fortnight and obtained a valuable series of birds. Three days' further march brought us to a place (10,500 ft) from which we were able to reach the highest mountains. We climbed above the snow-line on to the ice-cap of Mt Carstensz on the 30th of January and the 1st of February, but on neither occasion were we able to reach the summit of the mountain (15,800 ft). Above 6,000 ft the character of the forest begins to change, the trees are of smaller size and herbaceous plants are more numerous. About 8,000 ft are many Casuarinas, which are replaced higher up by bushy heaths and various flowering shrubs, until at about 11,000 ft the rocks become so steep as only to support the scantiest vegetation. In the higher regions (above 6,000 ft) animal-life was very scanty. Small parrots in pairs are seen occasionally, and large flocks of lories were found feeding on the fruits of the pandan trees up to 8,000 ft. A pair of pipits was seen in the rocky bed of a stream at 9,000 ft, and the droppings of a strange game-bird, probably the *Anurophasis monorthonyx* obtained by Mr Lorentz on Mt Wilhelmina, were noticed at 10,300 ft. Beyond that point the only birds seen were a pigeon (*Gymnophaps albertisi*), a sun-bird, and a rock-thrush. No birds of prey were seen above 6,000 ft. Insects are remarkably scarce and mammals are very few in the higher regions. A pair of Black Phalangers were caught at 8,000 ft by natives, who refused to part with them. On the ridges about 10,000 ft were seen many tracks of *Echidna*, and on the rocks above 13,000 ft were found the droppings of a carnivorous mammal.

Mr Ogilvie-Grant exhibited a nearly complete set of birds procured by Mr Wollaston and Mr Kloss during their ascent of Carstensz Peak. The collection, numbering nearly 1,300 specimens, had been received and unpacked two days previously, and it had therefore only been possible to examine them in a somewhat cursory manner; but in most instances the species had been provisionally named. As would be seen from the splendid series of birds displayed on the long table down the middle of the room, the number of species obtained was very large, and it would be difficult to find any country, other than New Guinea, which could boast of an avifauna so varied or so brilliant in colour. Many very rare and interesting species not to be found in any museum in Britain had been obtained. Some, such as the giant flightless rail *Megacrex inepta* D'Albertis and Salvadori, had already been described, but the addition to the National Museum of such a striking form was, in the opinion of the speaker, a far more important event than the discovery of a new species.

This great rail bore a curious resemblance to the members of the South American genus *Aramides*, but was of a much heavier build and evidently entirely dependent on its cursorial powers, being incapable of flight. Among the paradise-birds and bower-birds the attention of the members was especially drawn to *Loboparadisea sericea* Roths., represented by adult and immature birds of both sexes, and hitherto unrepresented in the British Museum. There were also exhibited adult examples, both male and female, of *Astrapia splendidissima* Roths., *Parotia carolae meeki* Roths., *Loria loriae* Salvad., etc. A new species, *Paradigalla intermedia*, with its nest and nestling, had also been obtained, the latter having the wattles on the sides of the face almost as well developed as in the nearly adult male. The splendid *Xanthomelas ardens* procured by the last expedition to the Mimika had not again been met with.

Among the parrots there were fine examples of the recently described *Aprosmictus wilhelminae* O.-Grant, proving that this form is well-characterised by its black mantle, also examples of *Cyclopsittacus godmani* O.-Grant, *Charmosynopsis multistriata* Roths., and many fine species of Passeres.

[Then follow the descriptions of four species apparently new to science.]

21

Expedition to Sikkim, 1930–31

From the report on the Club's meeting on 14 October 1931.

Mr Herbert Stevens gave an account of a journey to the Himalaya during the cold season of 1930–1931:

Throughout the last cold season I worked the Sikkim Himalaya for mammals and birds. Familiar with the physical features of the country and local conditions by my previous long residence, I decided to fix camps at various altitudes, and, by confining myself to a more or less limited area, employ the time to the best advantage. The results amply justified the seven months I was occupied.

My choice lay in the direction of the well-known trade route to and from Tibet which traverses eastern Sikkim, but preparatory to crossing the political frontier, preliminary collecting was undertaken in the foothills, and in order to obtain specimens of such species that do not even reach the base of the hills, a commencement was made in the plains at Haldibari in Cooch Behar. Hereabouts *Cisticola* in the grass lands, with the Brown Hawk-owl (*Ninox scutulata*) and the Little Scaly-bellied Green Woodpecker (*Picus vittatus myrmecophaneus*) within the limits of the village, were possibly of most interest. Leaving, after a fortnight's stay, Sevoke, in the Terai, was reached on October 22, 1930. Situated in the malarial belt, with a bad reputation in consequence, and unusually unhealthy towards the termination of the rains, it was not surprising that sickness made its appearance amongst my boys. However, this camp was only vacated after a month's work in the heavy forest, which is the habitat of the Large Hornbill (*Dichoceros bicornis*) and Tickell's Flycatcher-warbler (*Seicercus cantator*), while the dense undergrowth provides shelter for the Kalij Pheasant (*Gennaeus melanotus*) at its lowest distribution limit, and numerous Timaliidae, such as *Malacocincla* and *Pellorneum*. Mr G.E. Shaw, quinologist of the government Cinchona Plantations at Mungpoo, lost no time in renewing an old friendship. Professor Percy Moore, of Philadelphia, a collaborateur of the fauna volume on Hirudinae, also accepted my primitive hospitality in order to study the life-history of his favourite animals – the land-leeches – with which the place abounded, though other less obtrusive and insignificant pests were, in my experience, equally, if not more, troublesome.

From November 19 to December 28 a profitable time was spent at Mungpoo. Out of all the specimens obtained, the Spotted Wren (*Elachura formosa*) and the Forest Eagle-owl (*Huhua nipalensis*) were the most welcome. Descending, a camp was fixed below Sangsir in the Tista Valley, where the Long-tailed Sibia (*Heterophasa picaoides picaoides*) and several woodpeckers, including *Gecinulus grantia*, the Pigmy Blue Flycatcher (*Nitidula hodgsoni*), *Phyllergates coronatus, Yuhina nigrimenta, Baza jerdoni* and many others were

22

obtained. Ascending to Mungsong, at 4,500 feet, during a brief visit, we were fortunately favoured in the weather, as it is from a point a few yards away from this residence that the finest view of 'the snows' is obtainable in the Darjeeling district, embracing as it does the maidan at Rangpo, 1,200 feet, the only level ground in Sikkim with all the alternating mountain ranges, culminating in the summit of Kinchingunga and its sister peaks. Unfortunately this is only known to a limited few. Rail-head having been left behind at Kalimpong Road, I was dependent upon human transport, also employing bullock carts whenever these useful but tardy vehicles could be obtained. In spite of an overturned cart on quitting camp, everything arrived in due course at Rangpo, where a halt of two days allowed time to make further arrangements. A long-delayed thunderstorm, evidently quite local, compensated, if it did deluge the camp, in the opportunity afforded for observing a small party of the Red-legged Falconet (*Microhierax caerulescens*) contentedly preening themselves at daybreak alongside. The Ibis-bill (*Ibidorhyncha struthersii*) in its winter quarters frequented the shallows of the Rangpo River shortly before it joins the Tista.

Having commandeered a scrap lot of ponies, and taking a little-used route, a delightful open valley was traversed, and by evening Rarathang was reached. On January 25 I passed through Rongli, but not without the ever-recurring remonstrances from the ghorawallahs, invariably a difficult class of men to deal with. Refusing to listen to all arguments, and continuing on my way, the crowded bazaar, with all its attractions to my retinue, offered but a brief halt, and on arriving at a break in the road about two miles above Lingtam, camp was pitched on the cobbled surface, no more suitable ground being available. Now that I was once more firmly established my misgivings were soon dispelled, and the site proved to be ideal for my purpose, the only drawback to tranquility of mind being the everlasting roar from the torrent. The elevation of this camp was 5,250 feet. The orange-carriers, frequently met with labouring under ponderous loads, were now replaced by droves of likewise heavily laden mules transporting the season's wool-crop to Kalimpong, which must, however, have offered only a small margin of profit, and most of which might well have been burnt to advantage. Constant fluctuation, due to changes in temperature, was obvious in the number of local migrants, such changes also making the resident species move farther afield. From this camp were obtained *Machlolophus spilonotus, Garrulax albogularis, Dryobates cathpharius, Chrysophlegma flavinucha, Cutia nipalensis, Pteruthius melanotis, Haematospiza sipahi, Spinus thibetanus* (a rare Siskin in collections), and even *Troglodytes nipalensis* down to 5,000 feet, besides *Pachyglossa melanozantha* and *Dicaeum ignipectus*, the two last-named being obtained on gnarled trees festooned in the highest branches with mistletoe, the viscid seeds of which epiphyte *Pachyglossa melanozantha* can miraculously swallow but not digest. The most attractive tree, widely scattered in this locality, was the 'Gurupis' (*Leucosceptrum canum*), with a sweet nectar in its bottle-brush-shaped flowered stamen, which was frequented by sunbirds and barbets and other species too numerous to mention. In addition there were species of *Gennaeus* and *Tragopan* and *Arborophila rufogularis*, and, to my surprise, *Arborophila mandellii*.

A rise of 7,500 feet on the next march, only nine miles, brought me to my next site, and although dependent upon snow for water, there was no lack of rhododendron for firewood. After enduring the raging wind and extreme cold for two days and nights, at my request the villagers in Gnatong gladly came to the rescue, and, descending to 12,300 feet, the sanctuary of the rest-house was gained on March 5. The weather did not improve, and for real severity at high altitudes in my experience March and April are quite the worst months. The interminable mist rolled up almost daily, when a glorious morning's sunshine of a few hours duration was the last for that day. Apart from crows and the Griffon Vulture in numbers, ever alert for the carcase of a dying mule, with the solitary Lammergeyer not far away, was a single pair of *Prunella rubeculoides*, with a small party of *Laiscopus himalayanus*, which soon moved below the snowline. *Fringilauda nemoricola*, which later appeared in vast flocks, was there, and odd individuals of the Wren (*Troglodytes nipalensis*) and Blue-fronted Redstart (*Phoenicurus frontalis*). Once the ice thawed on the only stream fed from two small tarns, *Cinclus cashmeriensis* put in an appearance. While there was a paucity of bird-life in the pine forest, the usual Crested Tits, Creepers, and Bush-Robins (*Ianthia hyperythra*), too shy for near approach, could generally be met with. *Conostoma aemodium*, rare, of course, occupied the bamboo thickets along with *Ithaginis* and *Lophophorus*.

A large influx of migrants appeared with a brief break in the weather for the better, when pairing was in evidence. The scrub was crowded with *Phoenicurus frontalis* and *P. schisticeps*, and *Prunella strophiata*, an adept skulker, was equally plentiful. About this time *Perissospiza carnipes* and *Procarduelis rubescens* had separated into pairs, and from the topmost branches sang with a note by no means to be despised. With the exception of odd Buzzards, invariably melanistic specimens, and the Raven, obtained at Kappu, 13,000 feet, one of a solitary pair, little else was seen, though a pair of *Aquila nipalensis* had deserted the adjacent hills.

Returning on my tracks, camp was pitched at Jeluk, 9,200 feet, which was occupied from April 3–21. Hardly a day passed without a thunderstorm, often accompanied by hail, terrifying in grandeur, and had it not been known that phenomenal heat prevailed over the plains, the S.W. monsoon might have burst. Situated on a ridge, the flanks of the densely forested hills rose almost sheer behind. A warm pocket of air was evident within the ravine, where, on an extremely limited shelving patch of ground, overgrown with maling bamboo and interspersed with a few trees, a varied assemblage of birds occurred for a brief hour or so which allowed of ample discrimination in collecting. I do not recollect seeing any concourse similar in number and variety. This was in a measure accounted for by pressure from ascending migrants, agitated movement being evident with the approach of the breeding season.

While *Siphia strophiata* commonly haunted the moss-covered trees frequented by *Sibia nipalensis*, *Yuhina gularis*, *Yuhina occipitalis*, and *Dryobates darjellensis*, in the bamboo growth occurred *Suthora poliotis humii*, *Xiphoramphus superciliaris*, and *Ianthia indica*, and hereabouts one also obtained *Propyrrhula subhimachala*, *Pnoepyga albiventer*, *Homochlamys major*, and *Tickellia hodgsoni*. *Pyrrhula erythrocephala*, newly arrived, augmented *Æthopyga nipalensis* and *Pericrocotus brevirostris*, which already had nests, but suffered from the destructive forces of nature. Ticks had proved to be an intolerable nuisance at this altitude and lower.

Continuing on the descent, on reaching moderate altitudes numerous summer migrants, less conspicuous than *Stoporala thalassina*, were on their breeding-grounds, while the air rang with the noise of barbets and cuckoos. A brief halt was made at Rongli for a few days, and then back to Rangpo. Here I paid the penalty of delay, waiting for a motor-car faithfully promised to be repaired to time. Had I known this I would have preferred to complete my journey on foot. Ascending once again to Mungpoo, the Forest-Bittern (*Gorsachius melanolophus*), not previously recorded for Sikkim, was observed. All the several consignments sent down from my various camps, with what were in my care, were duly packed and left with me for Calcutta on May 4, 1931.

Considering the Sikkim Himalaya is about three-fifths the size of Wales, a total of 556 species and subspecies known to occur within these limits is surprising. Actually this number represents the avifauna in the basin of a single valley, with its subsidiary offshoots, as every stream in Sikkim State finds its way into the Tista, apart from the headwaters of a few minor streams to the east, which rise hereabouts, and the streams of the lower foot-hills in the Darjeeling district. The absence of the Nutcracker and the rarity of *Horeites brunnifrons*, plentiful on the outer ranges during the breeding season, to mention but another, *Myzornis*, which certainly did not occur in the tract worked, proves my contention that some species are extremely local, though often numerous in the locality where they occur. Since Mandelli enriched the National Collection, in 1873–79, *Indicator*, *Sphenocichla*, and *Callene* remain to be rediscovered in their habitat. As two of these species are probably resident, some future collector will locate them, if they have not entirely disappeared, but it will only be by intensive collecting over a limited area. I feel I was fortunate to locate *Arborophila mandellii*, as its habitat had baffled others as well as myself. My field-notes are not available, but probably they will be incorporated in the results when published.

Expedition to the Sudan, 1939

From the report on the Club's meeting on 11 October 1939.

Mr. J.D. Macdonald gave a talk as follows on his trip to the Sudan, and showed a large number of photographs:

About the end of last session I was on my way back from a bird-collecting expedition to the southern Sudan. Though my duties as a member of the staff of the Natural History Museum are primarily curatorial, I had been given the opportunity to gain field experience.

Tonight I should like to tell you a little about that expedition. I want to be brief, and not too technical.

Col. F.O. Cave, who is known to most of you, started it. We had hoped to be here together tonight, and I am sure he would wish me to apologise for his absence. The identification of a large collection made by him in the southern Sudan, and presented to the museum, revealed the fact that certain areas would probably repay more intensive study. Col. Cave was unable to undertake this himself, and suggested that I should do it. The suggestion had the sanction and support of the museum trustees and of the Sudan government.

Perhaps I should admit here that even now I make no claim to be a field ornithologist. About a year ago I was on a Nile steamer between Khartoum and Juba with a large quantity of collecting equipment, including guns and a rifle, the use of which I had practically no knowledge. I had only fired a light shotgun about three times. Perhaps it was a good omen that under quite difficult conditions I shot a crocodile while it was basking on a muddy bank. It was some weeks later before I was shown how to sight the rifle. But it had belonged to that most famous of African big-game hunters, Captain Frederick Selous, and probably, like the tippler's pony which would not be driven past a public house, the rifle refused to fire wide.

The areas which for various reasons we thought would repay more careful study are several mountain groups lying in the extreme south-east corner of the Sudan. The Imatong and Dongotona Mountains and the Didinga Hills lie on the Sudan border of Kenya and Uganda, and the Boma Hills are close to Abyssinia, much further away. The first three in particular form one of the many rather heterogeneous units which go to make up the Anglo-Egyptian Sudan. They are quite different to everything else. Therein lay the possibility of finding interesting birds.

These groups of mountains are literally islands in a wide expanse of flat country, which in the main is flooded during part of the year, and for the remainder is exceedingly dry, and in which vegetation is not very luxuriant. But above a certain altitude conditions are such as to maintain very dense forest. In the eastern limits, in particular, the cap of forest on the mountain tops is very striking. To me it seemed rather topsy-turvy to climb from barren plains and bone-dry watercourses into a region of streams and damp luxuriant forests. It was the birds of these forests in which I was particularly interested.

Very roughly the Imatong Mountains cover an area of 1,000 square miles, and rise quite abruptly to over 10,000 feet from about a 4,000-foot plain. I spent about six weeks there, collecting at various altitudes. On the first day of this year I was on the top of the highest peak, Mount Kineti. The commonest birds there were migrating pipits. I camped within sight of this mountain, at 9,000 feet, for about three weeks. The place was called Kipia. All that was there were two rather weather-beaten mud and wattle huts, remaining to testify to a former DC's love for the high hills.

Kipia was a first love, and I became very attached to it, though I arrived there cold and wet on Christmas day of last year, and had a miserably lonely dinner of sardines and tea. The scenery was very homely, though it was lacking in lochs. There was often hoar frost on the ground vegetation. I thrived under these conditions, though most of my camp developed chest colds. A native soldier lent me by Cave, and on whom I relied for keeping the camp together, had a temperature of over 100° for two days. It nearly resulted in a general strike. For all that, I became familiar with most of the birds, and made a representative collection.

There is an amusing story about a rain-gauge which Cave asked me to set up at Kipia. I had it officially unveiled on the first day of January, and as I could not return there myself on the 1st of February I arranged with an ex-soldier to come up from his village and change the bottles, taking the used one to Cave's headquarters at Torit, some two or three days' journey away. He was thoroughly drilled in the changing of the bottles, and particularly impressed with the necessity of not interfering with the quantity of water, even at the risk of incurring the wrath of his rain-gods. We know for a fact that there had been very little rain at Kipia after I left, but I was told that the native appeared at Torit with a record of about two or three hundred inches – the bottle was full to the cork. The loss of the record was perhaps compensated for by the insight into the native's mental processes.

The journey I had on leaving Kipia was one of the most difficult in my experience. The track had not been used for a long time, and little seemed to be known about it. According to my fount of information, Cave's soldier, Waka, it would take six hours to reach our next camping place. My Effendi assistant from Khartoum was equally certain it would only take four. It seemed, therefore, as if it could be accomplished quite easily between break-fast and lunch, so I parted from my baggage. But it took ten hours, and taught me several lessons I did not readily forget.

In the three weeks at Kipia I had become familiar with most of the birds there. I could identify almost everything I saw and heard. The camp I moved to from there was at 5,000 feet. At a certain point in the journey down we had

27

to negotiate an uncomfortably steep 300-foot rock-face at the 8,000-foot level. At the foot I found myself in a country with quite different vegetation, and strange birds I thought I should never get to know. This example of zonation was very striking. Incidentally, the area I came to then yielded a number of very interesting finds.

Early in February I set off for the Abyssinian border, about 200 miles away from the Imatongs. My headquarters there was the military post of Towat, in the Boma Hills. I was very fortunate in being able to go there as the area was not open to the casual traveller. The region is an escarpment of the main Abyssinian massif which has been cut off by the Sudan boundary. In getting there one crosses probably one of the richest and least-known game areas in Africa. I have heard first-hand accounts of game quantities almost difficult to believe, and though I crossed there at worst season I was amazed at what I saw even then. In a recent letter Cave told me that he flew over a herd of Cob stretching for ten miles.

Hardened travellers though most of you must be, I am sure you carry a vivid remembrance of some particular experience. I think the one that will live longest with me was that first view of the hazy blue line of the Boma Hills, rising out of a parched and blistering hot thornbush plain. It seemed as if it was the goal of a traditional pioneering urge, as well as promised satisfaction for the immediate bodily needs of water and cool shade.

But from a bird point of view the area was rather disappointing. The tops of the hills at 4,000 to 5,000 feet, though they towered over the interminably flat 1,800-foot plain, were not higher than the base of the Imatongs. In February the country was almost waterless, and seemed lifeless. I remember spending a whole morning in a patch of wood, and only saw or heard one bird. I had to work pretty hard for what I got, and was fortunate in making one or two interesting discoveries.

Perhaps one of my most interesting finds had no connection with ornithology. It was a new record for the Sudan in the form of two Italians who thought fit to penetrate into this region from south-west Abyssinia. They had come through a very inhospitable bit of country, and the opinion was that they had done well to survive on their wits for 38 days. I heard rumours that others were less fortunate. They had an Abyssinian boy and a woman with them.

At this time I was camping near a Kichepo village. The women of this people make 'saucers' of their lips. They seemed to be very self-conscious about their appearance. This tribe was unadministered, and very independent. They had to be handled with care and they were liable to flare up, particularly so at this time, as there was a great deal of unrest caused by the infiltrations of people from south-west Abyssinia. We had an exchange hunt one day. They first took me to shoot a hartebeest, and then I had the pleasure of watching them stalk and spear one. It was carried out with amazing skill. A few nights later I thought I was being given the same treatment. We had an exciting hunt near my tent, but discovered it was only a hyena after bird remains. On another occasion I was dozing in the shade of a tree when Waka propped up my rifle within easy reach. I asked him why, and he replied that I might need it. Apparently there had been a bit of trouble, but there was no worse damage than a gashed knee.

By the end of February I was back on the Uganda border, on the Didinga Hills, and within sight of the Imatong Mountains. I should explain that these two mountains, along with the smaller Dongotona Mountains in between them, lie close together, but are without any common foothills. They are exactly like islands.

The top of the Didinga Hills is an extensive plateau at about the 6,000-foot level. The scenery is rather like English downland, and it enjoys a delightful climate. At about 2,000 feet lower it is quite different to the top of the Imatongs. In fact, the only cloud forest exists as a cap on the top of Mount Lotuke, which rises to a 9,000-foot peak, and is connected to the extreme southern end by a narrow ridge. I camped on this ridge and just under the forest cap for about three weeks. The sides of the mountain are very steep, and the forests are literally impenetrable except with the aid of expert wood-craft. I had to have a path cut to the rather striking pinnacle at the top. I believe I was the first to ascend to the true summit. It was on the way back from one of these climbs that what is probably a typical Highland idiom of prompting a question in the negative nearly landed me in difficulties. I put a question to an English-speaking soldier in this way: 'It'll not be possible to go down that way, will it?' His reply, 'Yes, sir,' was perhaps logical, but it was at least disconcerting, and when I recovered myself he learned some more bad English in the form of good Scots.

I spent six weeks on the Didinga Hills and then Cave joined me for a short exploration of the Dongotona Mountains, where we again made a very interesting collection. Finally I got back to Torit about the middle of April, and during the rest of the month spent part of the time in going over the whole collection in Cave's 'Bird-room', and in going out for short trips into the field. But the most unique experience of all was to be flown by Cave over the mountains. He took me up on several occasions, and we were able to make a fine series of photographs to supplement those taken on the ground. It gave one a wonderful feeling of complete conquest to swoop and soar over many miles of country in which one had toiled and sweated for many weeks.

I have tried to describe in barest outline the nature of the country in which I collected, and one or two outstanding experiences. Perhaps the photographs handed round will help to fill in the story. Very little has been said about the results of the expedition. All I am going to say is that I brought back about 1,000 birds, and when the collection is properly worked out I hope it will be possible to publish some observations.

In the meantime I think it can be said that the expedition was very successful. I am sure you will agree that it could hardly have been so unless it ran smoothly from beginning to end. Col. Cave saw to that with meticulous care.

Discovery of new species and subspecies

The vast majority of the accounts of the discovery of new birds, and their descriptions, that have appeared in the pages of the *Bulletin* are dry and factual, of interest now only to taxonomists who may need to consult them for technical reasons. The four that follow are of more peculiar interest because of the circumstances of their discovery. Three, a pheasant, a bird of paradise and the Congo Peacock, were remarkable new species whose discovery was based on a few feathers; the fourth, the Irish Coal Tit, was a bird much nearer home, one of the few forms endemic to the British Isles, not very remarkable in itself but a good example of the problems posed by subspecies.

Mikado Pheasant

Described by W.R. Ogilvie-Grant, Bull. Brit. Orn. Cl. *16:122–3 (1906).*

Calophasis mikado, sp. n.

This species is founded on the middle pair of tail-feathers of a Pheasant which inhabits Mount Arizan, Central Formosa.

Mr Goodfellow writes: 'I found these feathers in the head-dress of a savage, who had come to carry our baggage. He said he had killed it on Mt Arizan and that it was rare.'

The feathers, which are shaped like the middle pair of tail-feathers of *C. humiae*, are black, crossed by about twelve narrow grey bands, about 1.5 inches apart; they are very different from the tail-feathers of any known species of Pheasant. They are incomplete at the base, but measure about eighteen inches.
Hab. Mount Arizan, Central Formosa.

Mr Rothschild informs me that among the Mikado's collection of live animals and birds, at Tokio, there are said to be a pair of Pheasants from Formosa belonging to an undescribed species, which he has been trying, so far unsuccessfully, to acquire. The birds are said to be 'blue with red legs,' a description which might apply to the male of *Gennaeus swinhoei*.

* * *

Shortly afterwards, at the meeting on 16 October 1907, Rothschild described the adult male (the tail-feathers originally described being those of the adult female), and placed the bird in the genus *Phasianus*, as the only structural difference between *Calophasis* and *Phasianus* was in the number of tail-feathers (sixteen in the former, eighteen in the latter), which Rothschild did not consider to be sufficient for generic separation. The Mikado Pheasant is now placed in the closely related genus *Syrmaticus*; it is considered vulnerable, with a population of perhaps a few thousand, but is still locally numerous and much of its habitat is precipitous and difficult of access (Johnsgard, *The Pheasants of the World*, 1986).

Ribbon-tailed Astrapia, *Astrapia mayeri*

From the report on the Club's meeting on 11 January 1939.

Mr C.R. Stonor exhibited and described:

Astrapia mayeri, sp. nov.

Description. Known only from two central rectrices, three other rectrices, two secondaries, and one greater wing-covert of a male. The two central rectrices are 81.6 cm in length, pure white for most of their length, and tipped with dark brown. The brown colour commences 3.5 cm from the tip, and the transition from it to the white of the rest of the feather is abrupt. The terminal 11 cm of the shaft is brown, as is also a very narrow strip of the vane on each side of it. These two feathers are sharply pointed, and the vane is extremely narrow relative to the total length, giving them a ribbon-like appearance; the average width is about 2.2 cm. The total length is slightly greater than the figure given, as they had been broken off above the point of the quill.

The other three rectrices are 12, 10, and 7.5 cm in length, sharply pointed, and dark brown in colour. There is evidently a very great disproportion between the two central feathers and the rest of the tail. The secondaries and greater wing-covert are dark brown, spangled with purple on the upper surface, as in the males of many Paradise Birds.

Distribution. At present rests on two field-records: from the vicinity of Mt Champion on the northern border of Papua; and eighty to a hundred miles west of Mt Hagen in the Mandated Territory.

Type. In British Museum (Natural History). Feathers taken by a missionary from the head-dress of a native on Mt Hagen, North-east New Guinea (*see below*).

Type-locality. Vicinity of Mt Champion; where first observed by Hides.

Remarks. The history of this remarkable bird is well told in a letter from Mr F. Shaw Mayer, written at Singapore on December 16, 1938. He says:

> I am sending you two tail-feathers of a new Bird of Paradise (*Astrapia?*). Briefly the history of the white-tailed bird; the first mention of a new Bird of Paradise, is in the late J.G. Hides's book *Papuan Wonderland* published 1936; on p. 106: 'As I stood in the branches of this tree gazing at the rock and heather-covered summit of the peaks in front of me, I noticed pairs of an interesting species of paradise birds flitting through the moss-covered branches of the trees around me. The males had two long ivory-white feathers as a tail, with which they made flicking noises as they trailed the plumes after them through the air. I did not know the species, so for the information of our ornithological department, I instructed one of the police to shoot a male bird, remove the tail-feathers, and carefully pack them away.

Mr Shaw Mayer continues:

> On this expedition Mr Hides was accompanied by Mr O'Malley, a patrol officer. In December of last year I met Mr O'Malley and questioned him about the birds.
>
> He remembered them quite well, and described the bird as being black in some lights and showing colours in others. Very true of the *Astrapias*. I was able to show him my live Princess Stephanie's (*A. stephaniae*), and he agreed they were very like these birds, only the body was a little smaller and, of course, had the two long white tail-feathers. He could not tell me what happened to the two feathers they brought back. He said the beak was short and not long like that of my live *Epimachus*. In May of this year I had a long talk with the Fox brothers, two New Guinea miners, who also made a remarkable journey of some hundreds of miles through the wild country west of Mt Hagen.
>
> They remembered meeting the white-tails well, some eighty to a hundred miles west of Mt Hagen. The natives of that part wore the tail-feathers in their hair.
>
> The Fox brothers' memories were better, as they thought these feathers had a black tip. They described the bird much as O'Malley did, and remarked about the flicking of the tail-feathers. They brought nothing back, but thought one of their boys might have saved a feather or two from a native's head. However, nothing turned up.
>
> In the middle of last August I was given by a missionary the two tail-feathers I am sending you. They were taken out of the hair on the head of a Mt Hagen native. The bird is *not* found, though, in the Mt Hagen district, but about eighty to a hundred miles west of it. It was a very great joy to see the feathers. I was surprised to find them so narrow ... I give the feathers to the Museum quite freely.

Affinities. As Mr Shaw Mayer suggests, there seems no doubt that this most interesting discovery belongs to the genus *Astrapia*. In the extraordinary length of the two central tail-feathers it comes nearest to *A. stephaniae* of Eastern New Guinea; and from the relative shortness of the three other tail-feathers it is quite clear that it also resembles it in the excessive lengthening of the two central feathers in relation to the rest of the tail; in the other three species of the genus, although the tail is very long, it is evenly and regularly graduated. Although the bird is described as smaller than *A. stephaniae*, the two feathers sent are 16.3 cm longer than the average of three males of the latter species.

The coloration approximates very closely to the small *A. splendidissima*, wherein the two central rectrices have just the same pattern of white, tipped with dark brown. A suspicion of this is to be seen in *A. stephaniae*, where the proximal section of the feather-shaft is white, while the rest is dark as in *A. nigra* and *A. rothschildi*.

The two long feathers are quite unique by virtue of their extreme narrowness described above. This condition is quite the reverse of what is found in three of the other four species, which have the tail-feathers unusually broad. In *A. splendidissima* the two central feathers are distinctly narrow for the greater part of their length, but broaden out into a rounded lobe near the tip. Presumably their extraordinary form in the new species is connected with the display of the males.

It would appear, therefore, that the new bird is from the same stock as *A. stephaniae* and *A. splendidissima*, and this is borne out by the distribution as at present known, for the former species is found to the east, while *splendidissima* replaces it to the west.

It is just possible that the new bird may be the male of *Astrapia stephaniae feminina*, described by Neumann from females and an immature male in 1922; and which was taken about a hundred and twenty miles to the north-west of Mount Champion. But in *A. splendidissima*, the other member of the genus with white on the tail, this character is in *both* sexes: and since the male of the new species has considerably more white than *splendidissima*, it is hardly likely that the female has none at all, as is evidently the case with *feminina*, from Neumann's description. I consider that (as already suggested by Dr Stresemann, *Archiv f. Naturgesch.*, lxxxix, 1924) Neumann's bird will probably prove to be the female of another new species, the male of which is as yet undiscovered.

In view of the trouble he has taken to establish its existence, and as a slight recognition of the efforts he has made during the past few years to add to our knowledge of the family as a whole, it is a pleasure to name this most striking new bird after its discoverer, *Astrapia mayeri*, Shaw Mayer's Bird of Paradise.

Congo Peacock

From the report of the Club's meeting on 13 January 1937.

Dr James P. Chapin exhibited the type-specimen and made the following remarks on:

The discovery of *Afropavo congensis*

This story has already been told in some detail in the *Revue de Zoologie et de Botanique Africaines*, xxix, Nov. 1936, pp. 1–6; but as I show you the two mounted specimens, the only ones yet known, I may be permitted to repeat a few of the salient facts.

No one, surely, could have suspected that such a bird existed in the Congo forest except myself, and that only because in 1913 I had found a single secondary quill, adorning a native hat, at Avakubi, in the Ituri Forest. For twenty-six years I was puzzled by that feather, and preserved it carefully. In 1921 I brought it to Europe, together with a number of other feathers collected in the same way, but nowhere was I able to match it, nor were any of my friends able to offer any suggestion as to its origin. At one time I was almost ready to announce that Africa must harbour a large gallinaceous bird still unknown, and then my courage must have failed me, for I did nothing.

When at last I happened upon two mounted specimens, without locality, in the Congo Museum, where they had been since 1914, I felt confident from the start that they could not be hybrids of any sort, mainly because of my feather. Within a few days I had additional evidence from Monsieur de Mathelin de Papigny, who had eaten one in 1930 at Angumu, in the eastern Congo. At this place there is a gold-mine, located in the midst of a heavy forest that was almost without native inhabitants.

Monsieur de Mathelin was anxious that we should secure additional specimens, and at once communicated with the doctor stationed at the mine. We now have word that two black workmen there claim to have seen this Congo Peacock in the vicinity of Angumu during the month of December 1936; so there is every likelihood that within a relatively short time more specimens can be obtained. I even have hopes of being able to visit Angumu myself, in order to learn more about the haunts and habits of the bird, and to determine whether the bird found at Angumu is racially identical with the type.

Afropavo congensis is assuredly the most interesting new bird that has been discovered in Africa for many years past. Apart from Quails, Partridges, Francolins, and the Stone-bantam, no genus of Phasianidae (in the restricted sense) was previously known from tropical Africa. This bird, which I firmly believe to approximate an ancestral stage in the development of the true Peacocks, seems to be a left-over from the time when a broad area of equatorial rain-forest extended from West Africa to Burma and beyond.

Dr Percy Lowe said that as regards the stumps of what had doubtless been some sort of duplicate crest springing from the vertex of this interesting bird, he was as much at a loss to explain their morphology as the lecturer. They were disposed in small groups of four or five springing from a series of pits or fovea sunk apparently in the epidermal and subcutaneous tissues. With a pair of forceps he had taken hold of one of these stumps and had kept up a steady pull, with the result that in the end he pulled out a long and thick grass-like stem which measured 23 mm in length. Unless there was a deep frontal or parietal depression on the vertex of the skull it was difficult to say from whence such a specialised crest-feather, entirely devoid of barbs and barbules, and very stiff and hard, could have come, for in any ordinary bird of the same size and nature it was long enough to have penetrated well into the bird's brain. Although much thicker and stronger, they reminded him of the crest-plumes seen on the head of a Crowned Crane; but their actual appearance in the bird suggested that they had been cut off or removed at the level of the skin by some outside agency.

Dr Chapin in his description of this remarkable new bird had alluded to the Pheasant-like *Lophura*. This reminded the speaker that in a paper published in *The Ibis* of 1933, pp. 340–41, he had suggested that the fossil bones found in the Miocene of France, and referred by Milne-Edwards to the genus *Phasianus* (*Ph. altus, medius,* and *desnoyersi*), and subsequently by Lambrecht to a new genus *Miophasianus*, might more properly be referred to the genus *Lophura*. He had suggested this on account of the remarkably long tarso-metatarsus which characterised these fossil species.

Afropavo had similarly a very long tarso-metatarsus, and although he did not for a moment suggest that *Afropavo* was a *Lophura*, the thought occurred to him that these Miocene so-called Pheasants of France might equally well have been generalized Peacocks or *Lophuras*. The Miocene period in France was characterised by a tropical climate and fauna, and as the climate became colder in the Pliocene and subsequent periods, the way to warmer conditions in Africa was open to the fauna by means of land bridges across the Mediterranean. Might not the Ituri Forest represent the last sanctuary of a generalised Peacock which formerly lived in Europe?

* * *

Because of its rarity, no specimens of *Afropavo* have been available for analysis by DNA hybridisation or any other recently developed biochemical technique. From an anatomical examination, P.R. Lowe (1938, *Proc. 9th Int. Orn. Congr.*: 219–30) tentatively concluded that it is an 'unspecialised generalised or primitive peacock', closest to the 'Pavoninae and Argusianinae'.

Irish Coal Tit

From the report on the Club's meeting on 14 December 1910.

Mr W.R. Ogilvie Grant exhibited and described examples of a new species of titmouse from Ireland.

He said that it might seem almost incredible that an extremely distinct and well-marked species of Irish titmouse should have escaped notice until the present time; nevertheless, such was undoubtedly the case.

Of this new species, which he proposed to call *Parus hibernicus*, he had now

36

examined twelve adult examples from the following counties: Dublin, Wexford, Waterford, Westmeath, and Sligo. Knowing that the Natural History Museum was extremely deficient in examples of Irish birds, Mr Collingwood Ingram had kindly forwarded a few specimens from Boyle, Co. Sligo, and, among them, two Coal-titmice, which Mr Ogilvie-Grant had at once recognised as belonging to a species quite distinct from *P. britannicus*. Mr Ingram was unaware that there was any particular interest attaching to the birds, and it seemed extraordinary that no one had hitherto noticed the striking characteristics of the Irish titmouse.

The pale mustard colour of the patches on the sides of the head and occipital spot, as well as of the breast and belly, also the clear cinnamon-coloured sides, flanks, and upper tail-coverts, rendered *P. hibernicus* distinguishable at a glance from *P. britannicus*.

Through the kindness of Dr Scharff he had been able to examine five examples of the Irish titmouse, preserved in the National Museum of Ireland. One of these, a fine male example from Athlone, had been obtained as long ago as May 1865!

The species might be characterised as follows:

Parus hibernicus, sp. n.

Adult male. Differs from the male of *P. britannicus*, Sharpe & Dresser, in having the light patches covering the sides of the head and neck, as well as the occipital spot, pale mustard-yellow, the back olive-grey washed with yellowish-cinnamon, the upper tail-coverts cinnamon, in marked contrast with the rest of the upperparts, the breast and belly whitish, washed with mustard-yellow, and the sides and flanks cinnamon. Iris dark hazel; bill black; legs bluish-slate-colour.

Total length ca.4.3 inches; wing 2.45; tail 1.9; tarsus 0.75.

Adult female. Similar to the adult male, but smaller. Wing 2.2 inches.
Hab. Ireland.
Obs. In freshly killed examples the mustard-yellow colour of the light patches on the sides of the head, occiput, and underparts was very bright and conspicuous, but the colour faded considerably a few days after death.

There could be no doubt that the British Coal-titmouse also occurred commonly in one locality at least in the north-east of Ireland, for Mr Ogilvie-Grant had himself obtained a number of specimens at Clandeboye, Co. Down, in January 1904. These differed in no way from examples of *P. britannicus* from England and Scotland. He was not aware whether these birds bred in Co. Down, or were merely winter migrants from the opposite coast of Great Britain. Nothing more was known of the distribution of these two species of Coal-titmouse in Ireland, as very few Irish birds were at present available for comparison.

* * *

There are several points of interest about this extract. First, a minor technicality: it was published on 31 December 1910, but three days earlier the *Daily Mail* had published a short news item headed 'New British Bird/Yellow Coal Tit found in Sligo', containing the first mention of the name *Parus hibernicus* and a brief and not entirely accurate account of the bird and its discovery. Sir William Ingram, proprietor of the *Daily Mail*, was Collingwood Ingram's father, and authorised the article (very likely thinking that the *Bulletin* would be published first).

The *Daily Mail*'s priority has tended to be ignored in later publications, but is mentioned in Witherby's *Handbook*. Of more taxonomic interest is the fact that the Irish Coal Tit was described as a full species in the last days of the resistance in Britain to the adoption of trinomial nomenclature. In other countries, particularly in the United States, trinomials had come into general use many years earlier. Finally, the Irish Coal Tit exemplifies a common problem inherent in the use of trinomials and not yet resolved (not, in fact, resolvable). As Ogilvie-Grant noted, Coal Tits from County Down are indistinguishable from English and Scottish birds. There is presumably a cline of gradually decreasing yellowness of plumage from the southwest of Ireland towards the east, but it seems never to have been systematically investigated (see p. 105). There is no way of defining with any exactness the range of *Parus ater hibernicus*. One solution, proposed by Huxley (see p. 103), is to use the 'cline', with its associated symbol; but this too has its problems and has not been widely adopted. Nevertheless, the advantages of using trinomials outweigh the disadvantages.

Migration

Bird migration does not figure very prominently in the *Bulletin*, except in the nine special volumes published from 1906 to 1914. These were the fruits of an inquiry instituted by the Club in 1904. It was one of the first cooperative inquiries in the history of ornithology, and certainly the most ambitious of the early ones, pre-dated only by the migration inquiry organised by the British Association in the 1880s.

A subcommittee was set up in 1904, to inquire into the 'migration of birds within these islands' (including data collected from off-shore light-vessels). The first survey was carried out in the spring of 1905, and the inquiry continued for over eight years, covering nine spring and eight autumn migrations. The two extracts from the migration reports which follow need little comment. It is of interest that the method used was later adopted, in more refined form, by H.N. Southern in studies of the spring migration of some common species through Europe, and it remained a standard method for the study of migration until large-scale ringing and technically more sophisticated methods, such as radar, took over and led to advances which were impossible at the beginning of the century.

Report on the first season's work, 1905

Mr Bonhote, as Secretary to the BOC Migration Committee, presented the following report on the work done during the past season:

Gentlemen,
As this is our last Meeting this Session, we think it advisable to lay before you an interim report on the result of our work during the spring migration, which is just over.

We must first acknowledge with grateful thanks the great assistance and support we have received from observers throughout the country, who have willingly responded to the call made on them and have sent their schedules carefully filled in weekly.

The schedules were sent in from March 19th to June 4th, covering a period of just under three months, the height of the migration occurring during the weeks ending April 16th, 23rd, and 30th. The earliest migrant to arrive was the Wheatear on the 14th March, closely followed by the Chiff-chaff on the 18th of the same month; the latest migrant to arrive was the Nightjar, which, although first recorded during the last week of April, did not really arrive in numbers until the third week in May.

All schedules as they came in were carefully docketed and filed, their contents extracted, and sketch maps filled in showing the distribution of each species during the week. Some of these maps are brought up for your inspection here tonight.

Short weekly summaries were then made and sent round to each member of the committee.

It has been arranged to send copies of these summaries to all those who have kindly assisted, but, unfortunately, it has not been possible to get them printed by tonight; they are, however, ready for press and have been brought up for your inspection.

By the kind permission of the Trinity House authorities, the larger light-houses and lightships along the east and south coasts have been supplied with schedules, and a large number of wings, for which payment at the rate of 1d apiece has been made, have been received.

Although all this material has been filed and roughly identified, we have not yet started to work it out.

We propose to continue the lighthouse observations throughout the year, but not to resume land-operations until the next spring migration.

We now intend to devote ourselves to the careful and systematic working out of all the material received, and hope to lay our full report before you early in the next session.

As regards the financial aspect, the accounts for the season have not yet been completed, but we may state that after paying up everything there still remains a small balance over from the £20 granted for this purpose, which will, it is hoped, be more than sufficient to cover the cost of printing and sending out the weekly summaries, and thus completing our task for this season.

(*signed*)

> F.G. Penrose
> H.F. Witherby
> N.F. Ticehurst
> M.J. Nicoll
> J. Lewis Bonhote

On behalf of the Migration Committee, Mr H.F. Witherby exhibited the wings and legs of a Grey Shrike, of the form known as *Lanius major*, Pallas, taken at the Newarp lightship (Essex coast), on April 17, 1905, and of a Black Redstart, *Ruticilla titys*, taken at the Inner Dowsing light (Norfolk coast), on April 14, 1905.

Dr. F. Penrose proposed a vote of thanks to Mr Witherby and Mr Bonhote, who, he stated, were really responsible for the whole of the work which had been done by the committee.

Massive immigration of northern finches in autumn of 1910

The Mealy Redpoll (*Linota linaria*)

Amongst the immigrations of the less common northern species for which the autumn of 1910 was remarkable, those of the Mealy Redpoll were perhaps the most noteworthy, both on account of the extent of the area of arrival and of the vast numbers of birds that were concerned in them.

The area of arrival included the whole of the east coast from the northernmost Shetlands to Kent, the largest numbers apparently arriving in the Forth area, and on the coasts of Yorkshire, Norfolk and Kent.

The immigration commenced at the beginning of October, the first bird being taken at Dungeness Light (Kent) on the 3rd/4th, the first (dated) record from Shetland being on the 9th, though birds had been seen there for some days. At the end of the second week simultaneous arrivals were recorded in the Shetlands, the Isle of May and on the Yorkshire, Norfolk and Suffolk coasts, and from then onwards to the end of the month fresh arrivals were recorded daily at one or more points on the east coast. The immigration seems to have reached its height between the 26th and 30th and to have gradually waned during the first week of November.

What became of the birds after arrival there is very little evidence to show, apart from the fact that many (probably many thousands) were captured by bird-catchers at or near the coast. That many passed south along the east coast there is no doubt, as such movements were definitely recorded during the latter part of October and the first half of November; others, particularly those that landed in the Forth area, appear to have penetrated some distance to the west and south-west (Peebles, Lanark, Renfrew and Ayrshire) and even to Skye and the Inner Hebrides. From England, apart from the east coast, there were practically no records, and the birds do not seem to have passed further west along the south coast than Dungeness. Vast numbers were present on the south coast of Kent during the month of November, and fell a prey to the bird-catchers of that district as in others further north, but what eventually became of the remainder there was no evidence to show.

For a more detailed account of this invasion, so far as Scotland was concerned, reference may be made to a paper by Mr W. Evans in the *Proc. Roy. Phys. Soc. of Edinburgh*, xvii, no. 3.

Holböll's Redpoll (*Linota linaria holboelli*)

During the immigration of the Mealy Redpoll (*suprà*) numerous examples of this somewhat doubtful race were identified, and Mr W. Evans estimates that of some 2,000 or more birds that passed through the hands of Edinburgh dealers, about one-fourth belonged to this form. Others were recorded from Shetland, Fair Isle, the Isle of May, Haddington and Cambridge.

The Northern Bullfinch (*Pyrrhula major major*)

The arrival of a number of this northern form was a marked feature of the autumn migration of 1910.

The first two birds were taken at the Isle of May (Fife) on the 22nd of October; on the following day seven were seen in the neighbourhood of Lerwick (Shetland), and on the 24th the species was first noticed in Unst (Shetland). On the 24th and 25th single birds appeared on Fair Isle (Shetland), two more were taken on the Isle of May on the 26th, and others were seen on Fair Isle on the 27th and 29th. On the 29th, also, one was caught in East Lothian, while one was seen at Barnsness Light (Haddington) on the 31st. On the 2nd of November numbers arrived on Fair Isle, and another was taken at the Isle of May; one was seen in N. Unst on the 7th, another at Fair Isle on the 10th, and others at Lerwick on the 20th and 21st. At the end of the month one was caught at Berwick-on-Tweed, while others were reported from Fifeshire and from several places on the Yorkshire coast during November. On the 3rd of December one was shot on the S. Yorkshire coast, and on the 18th two more were seen at Lerwick.

Eagle Clarke's 'discovery' of Fair Isle

It was during the course of the BOC's migration inquiry, but working independently, that Eagle Clarke began his remarkable work on Fair Isle, as reported in the Chairman's address for 1908.

In the next place, as regards British ornithology, the most remarkable event during the past year [1907] has, I think, been Mr Eagle Clarke's successful investigation of Fair Isle. That such an insignificant rock should have received visits from so many rare birds seems to be little short of marvellous. Examples of not less than 117 species were obtained or observed by Mr Clarke and his assistants during the spring and autumnal migrations of 1907. Of these 17 were new to the avifauna of the islet, and amongst these were such rarities as the Siberian Chiffchaff (*Phylloscopus tristis*), the Black-headed Bunting (*Emberiza melanocephala*), the Black-throated Wheatear (*Saxicola stapazina*), and the Short-toed Lark (*Alauda brachydactyla*), whilst others, of less importance, were the Grasshopper-warbler (*Locustella naevia*), the Wood-warbler (*Phylloscopus sibilatrix*), and the Black Redstart (*Ruticilla titys*). It would almost seem that in Fair Isle we have found a British rival to the famous Islet of Heligoland at the mouth of the Elbe.

Migration on the Chinese coast

Also at the same time as the BOC's migration inquiry, J.D. La Touche, at the other side of the world, began to investigate the spectacular migration along the Chinese coast. After years of neglect, this important migration route has been studied again by a series of Cambridge expeditions starting in 1985.

A list of the species of birds
collected and observed in the
Island of Shaweishan by J.D. La Touche
revised and arranged by C.B. Rickett

Shaweishan is a rocky islet situated about thirty miles east of the mouth of the Yangtszekiang (lat. 31° 25' 22" N, long. 122° 13' 50" E). It is covered with brushwood, and on one side there are a number of medium-sized trees. There is also a lighthouse on the island.

Mr La Touche sent collectors to the island during the spring migrations of 1907, 1908, and 1911, and in the autumn of 1910. The records for the spring of 1907 are very imperfect, so that the word 'none' against that year must not in every case be taken to mean that the species did not occur, but simply that it was not recorded.

All figures up to ten are said by the collectors to be the actual number of birds seen, above ten the numbers are roughly approximate.

The following notes are extracts from records kept by T'ang Wang Wang, the head collector:

In spring, birds are very plentiful on the island when there is a north-west wind accompanied by drizzling rain.

In 1910 during the months of September to December great numbers of birds were passing from north to south. Those landing on the island were, in many cases, in a very exhausted state, and dozens of dead, in a very emaciated condition, were picked up. During this period he observed Peregrine Falcons preying largely on the migrants, more especially on Eastern Turtle-Doves, Quails, and Snipe.

The light-keepers told him that four or five years previously they saw large numbers of small birds taken by Sparrow-Hawks, and that the island was strewed with the feathers of their victims.

On the night of the 16th of October 1910, there was apparently a great influx of migrants. Numbers of birds passed the light and many struck about midnight; there was very little wind, the sky overcast, and rain falling. Among those taken at the light Wang noted one Sparrow-Hawk, some Grey Wagtails, one *Butastur indicus*, one *Pandion haliaëtus*, one *Lanius tigrinus*, one *Anthus gustavi*, one *Acrocephalus bistrigiceps*, one *Locustella lanceolata*, five *L. ochotensis*, and two *Hirundo gutturalis*.

On the 16th, 17th, and 18th of November in the same year a great number of small birds died of cold on the island. The principal sufferers apparently were *Turdus obscurus*, *Alauda arvensis cinerea*, and *Emberiza rustica*.

(The annotated systematic list follows.)

Migration at Ushant

From the report on the Club's meeting on 11 October 1933.

Colonel R. Meinertzhagen made the following remarks upon autumn migration at Ushant:

The island of Ushant, lying twelve miles off the west coast of Brittany, has proved itself to be a first-class observatory for bird migration. Dr Eagle Clarke visited it in 1898, but was only able to remain there some ten days owing to the misconstruction placed on his activities by the French authorities. Since the war, Collingwood Ingram visited the island for a short period of the autumn migration, during September, and made some valuable observations, also recording for the first time in Europe the occurrence of *Locustella fasciolata* from eastern Asia. We visited the island from September 11 to October 4, arming ourselves with a Naturalist's Permit from the French

Government, a Permis de Chasse, and a letter of recommendation from the authorities to the lighthouses. We were not molested in the slightest degree, and on all sides met with courtesy and kindness. One has to be devoted to crustaceans of every description to enjoy a visit to Ushant.

Ushant Island has been well described by Eagle Clarke in vol. ii, of his *Studies in Bird Migration*, 1912, pp. 305–28. It is, roughly, five miles by two, the longer axis running south-west and north-east. It is practically treeless, but contains small patches of scrub and a few small spinneys, sufficient, and, indeed, ideal, for sheltering migrants. Two shallow valleys running parallel into the Bay of Lampaul contain a few reed-beds and osier-beds. The rest of the island is open heath, stunted gorse, and heather, whilst at the south-west extremity is a fine stretch of short crisp grass, ideal for Wheatears, Dotterel, and suchlike birds. Wader-ground is poor, the bulk of the coast-line being granite rock, rugged and ragged. Lampaul Bay has a fair stretch of sand, and it was here that we saw the few Waders observed. We soon became well acquainted with the island, and our party of three made a rule of patrolling it thoroughly every day.

The local inhabitants and the lighthouse keepers had no bird sense, though quite prepared to give information on the purely sporting aspect. We were, however, credibly informed that on December 27, 1927, 416 Woodcock struck the Creoch Light, and many hundreds of exhausted birds were killed on the following day throughout the island. All the islanders were agreed that during the winter storms from November to March, especially when snow has fallen on the mainland, the island is visited by thousands of birds of all sorts. Unfortunately we have no accurate information on bird migration at Ushant except during the early part of autumn passage, in fact during the periods during which Eagle Clarke, Collingwood Ingram, and ourselves visited the island. Local information we found to be quite unreliable. One quite intelligent informant, after enumerating many species seen in winter, was asked, by way of a test, 'I suppose you get a few Turkeys here in hard winters?' 'Oh, yes,' he replied, without a smile; 'in very hard weather I have shot them, but they are rare.'

During the period of our visit we kept a migration chart which shows at a glance the volume of migration among sixteen of the commoner forms. What stands out from this chart is the response made by migrants to an east wind. It moved them from Ushant and caused others to arrive. Other winds had not the same effect, neither had the weather. The only influence fog, cloud, or clear weather seemed to have on passage was that in clear weather only tired birds would come down to Ushant, whilst during fog the main body would take advantage of the island.

Among the residents and summer visitors the Meadow-pipit, Stonechat, Yellow Hammer, Wheatear, Rock-pipit, Hedge-sparrow, Wren, House-sparrow, Sky-lark, Corn-bunting, Swallow, and Common Tern were the commonest. The Robin (continental form), Raven, Water-rail, and Moorhen are scarce. The Kestrel is probably resident, also the Ringed Plover. Notable exceptions are the Starling, Dartford Warbler, and Chough, all so common in Brittany. The Chough was seen occasionally, but these were only parties wandering from the mainland. The Stonechat is darker even than the British form (*Saxicola torquata hibernans*), and is much nearer the Hebridean form (*S. t. theresae*). The Hedge-sparrow and Robin are the continental forms.

This is no place for a detailed list of migrants. I shall only mention the rarer observations. Among interesting birds we secured a Firecrest on September 18 and saw another on the 25th. A Tawny Pipit was shot on September 18, a solitary bird. Dotterel were seen on September 14, 16, and 18. A specimen of the Melodious Warbler (*Hippolais polyglotta*) was obtained on September 22. Pairs of Grey Phalarope were seen on September 20 and 30. A few British Robins appeared on September 24, and were easily recognisable on colour and by habit. Whereas the resident Ushant Robin is a skulker and confined to bush and spinneys away from habitations, the British form, on arrival, kept close to habitations, and showed no fear of man. Sedge-warblers were common during most of our stay, and struck the Light in some numbers. The problem of the Kingfisher is interesting, for Eagle Clarke noted them as surprisingly abundant in September. We saw only a few individuals. They must certainly be migrants, and little seems to be known about the movements of this bird. Great Shearwaters were seen in August, when I spent a day at Ushant, and several were seen on October 4. A single Pied Wagtail was secured on September 28, though the White Wagtail was fairly common throughout our visit. Two Pratincoles were seen flying over on September 29, and a few Snow-buntings appeared on September 24 and 25 in a very tired condition.

Whence do these Ushant September migrants come? It is too early for the east-to-west European passage, and I am inclined to think they all come from a northerly direction. The occurrence of Snow-buntings and Greenland Wheatears would seem to support this view, whilst we never saw a single migrant which could for certain be said to be an east-to-west migrant. If this is correct it would then appear that the Firecrest, Melodious Warbler, and Tawny Pipit might be British breeding birds. But whence came the Pratincole?

There are two other aspects of migration which interested us. In the first place, the relation between moult and migration. We caught several individuals with primaries still in moult, and a good many in full body moult. But by far the majority of specimens handled showed no sign of moult, and had changed into winter plumage. Where moult was in progress birds were thin, otherwise they were all very fat. The other aspect of migration was stomach-contents of birds actually on passage, that is, birds which struck the Creoch Light. These comprised ten Sedge-warblers, three Whitethroats, a Tree-pipit, and three Dunlins. In every case there was not a trace of food in the stomach.

The nearest portion of the English coast to Ushant is about the south coast of Cornwall and Devon, a distance of 120 miles. When birds struck the Creoch Light it was always between 1 a.m. and 3.30 a.m., which still further lends support to the view that September passage in Ushant arrives from the north.

There are two lighthouses on Ushant Island and two on rocks just off its coast. The main light is the Creoch Light, at the south-west end, with a white beam. The other land lighthouse is at the north-east end, with a red beam. This red-beam light has never been known to attract birds.

Influx of continental Jays
into southern England

From the report on the Club's meeting on 13 November 1935.

Dr Lowe also remarked on a recent influx of Jays into Hampshire:

A very interesting movement of Jays has occurred this autumn in Hampshire, which doubtless some of you have heard about, and in which I know Mr Witherby is interested. Our first notification at the British Museum of this movement was contained in a letter to Mr Kinnear from Mr John Berry, written on October 5 of this year, who said that Mr Charles Stonor and himself had just been observing, between 8 and 9 a.m. that morning, a flock of between 250 and 300 Jays over New Hall, on the Itchen just outside Southampton, circling round and performing a series of acrobatics at a great height and suddenly swooping into some high trees, like Hawks 'stooping'. Mr Berry shot one (which he sent to the British Museum), but the shot did not seem to alarm the others; they continued to fly over his head, and displayed no fear. The flock was about for over three hours. The day was still and misty, but not foggy.

On October 8 Major Maurice Portal wrote me a letter saying that Hampshire had been cursed with an influx of Jays passing over too high to shoot. He enclosed a letter from a friend – Mr Alan Arnold – giving some details of this invasion. This letter was dated October 4, and Mr Arnold says:

'I was standing on the Winchester–Southampton road this morning at 9 o'clock, and a covey of Jays came over from the direction of this house, passing over the Home of Recovery entrance-gate, and flying towards Hutwood, about a gun-shot high. I counted them and there were 45; then they kept coming in fours and fives, and sometimes a few more in batches, and I counted up to 187 and had to leave. After the first covey they came higher and higher, and must have been 200 or 300 feet up, but you couldn't possibly mistake them for any other bird – all the early ones I could see quite plainly.

Major Portal says that:

> Here, viz., at Holywell, Swanmore, Southampton, on October 3rd, 37 Jays passed high up. On October 4th, 45 and 55 in two lots three miles off, but high up. Unfortunately none pitch in, but I'm sure some must drop in. Will you mind if you are sent up Jays for a bit? Of course, I suppose they will be our British Jays, but a keeper shot three on Sunday and fed to ferrets, and told me they were "wonderful tame" – which makes me wonder.'

Since these letters more communications from Major Portal have been received, and in one he relates how one keeper instructed to shoot Jays shot a number and did not send them 'because he knew they were British Jays, and so no good for the investigation being made at the Museum', which introduces the humorous element into the inquiry.

It is absolutely clear, then, on the face of things that there has been an influx of continental Jays into England because, apart from the evidence which I have briefly referred to, everyone seems to be agreed that these Jays are very tame, and anyone who shoots Pheasants will know that a keeper cannot be sent out to shoot Jays in England and make a bag of fifty. These, and other bags which have been made, are manifestly impossible with British Jays.

There seems to be only one possible or conceivable alternative, which I think can be ruled out of court at once, viz., that these Jays are British Jays which, owing to adverse conditions of one sort or another elsewhere, or even owing to too favourable conditions, leading to an abnormal increase in the local populations, have flocked together and wandered off in search of more favourable localities and circumstances. All the evidence seems against such a rather far-fetched idea. Besides, we know that previous influxes of Jays have occurred, notably on the east coast (Ticehurst). But you will all very naturally say: if you think these Jays are continental immigrants why not compare them with topotypical examples from Scandinavia, or with others from other continental countries, or with British or Irish specimens. Here you have just the very opportunity of making use of and justifying the work of systematists who have distinguished the Scandinavian, British, and Irish residents as distinct races.

Well, that is just what we have been trying to do. Mr Kinnear, thinking, no doubt, that I was more of an anatomist than a systematist, and therefore less likely to be biassed, asked me to undertake the inquiry.

Altogether about thirty-five of these immigrants have been skinned and compared with British, Scandinavian, Irish, and continental series. What has been the result? On the whole I think it has not been satisfactory; even with the aid of professed systematists accustomed and trained to appreciate the niceties of colour-tones.

Our series in the British Museum collection are perhaps not good enough, and there are various snags in the way. For instance, in the case of a British-killed series, with this present fresh evidence of a possible autumnal influx of continental examples it does not necessariy follow that all British-killed specimens are British born and so on. It therefore follows that our series, although so carefully labelled and dated, may be contaminated by wanderers. We want, so to speak, pure cultures or, in other words, series of pure natives or birds which we know have been bred in the different countries concerned.

At present, although you may have large series from different countries of autumn-killed birds spread out in a good light, I do not think that the identity of our thirty-five Hampshire immigrants could be said to be absolutely proved by the subspecies test; and the case is complicated by the similarity they present to Central European examples.

The case is also complicated by the fact that although in the mass series from different regions may be distinguishable, yet the identification of individuals is a proceeding so difficult, so nice, and so fortuitous as to give rise to the doubt as to the possibility of its being done, or, I may say, possible enough to be of practical use.

My conclusion, therefore, is that although we may feel absolutely certain in our own minds that these Jays came from somewhere on the Continent, our series of Jays from different countries is not perfect enough to justify us in making the statement that this has been proved by the subspecies test.

There is just one other point. Major Portal's series, after subtracting one or two examples which were probably British born, could in the mass be distinguished from Scandinavian and Irish examples, but the doubt has arisen in my mind if they can be distinguished from French or other continental birds.

In other words, I have begun to wonder if the area of distribution of this race, whatever it may be, may not include a slice of southern England as well as France, Belgium, and other countries.

* * *

Mr Witherby and others joined in the discussion, and Mr Witherby remarked that he considered the British Jay was a good race, and that it was possible some of the Jays sent to the British Museum were British-bred birds. The others may have come from some part of the Continent other than Scandinavia.

The Sooty Falcon *Falco concolor*

The following comparatively recent paper, by R.E. Moreau, seems worth reprinting in full, both because it deals with the migration of a most remarkable species, and because it is a prime example of Moreau's genius for organising and collating a mass of information from diverse sources and presenting it in a style all too rare in scientific papers.

From the Bulletin, *vol. 89 (1969): 62–7.*

The documentation of the Sooty Falcon is most unsatisfactory. That it is possible to do a clean-up of some value is due in part to Mrs B.P. Hall, who in conjunction with Derek Goodwin has examined the material in the British Museum (Natural History) for me and has kindly criticised this paper in draft. I am indebted also to Dr M.C. Radford and to John Yealland for consulting references for me that I could not reach myself, and to C.W. Benson, Captain H.E. Ennion, Dr C. Vaurie, Dr E. Stresemann, Major W. Stanford and Dr A. Zahavi for answering enquiries.

Biologically the Sooty Falcon is of extraordinary interest because it shares with Eleonora's Falcon the distinction of being the only species of bird that in any part of the north temperate zone starts to breed only after the summer solstice, an adaptation that enables it, like Eleonora's, to feed its young on the autumn migrants. I knew the bird in the 1920s, hunting bats over the Giza Zoological Gardens and also as liable to be seen at any hour of the day about the deeply dissected plateau east of the Nile in the neighbourhood of Cairo – cf. Goodwin's (1949) day-time record in similar country near Suez, where, he tells me, he saw a pair catch a Swallow in full daylight. Nicoll (1919) described it as 'a resident in small numbers in Lower and Upper Egypt'. What evidence then existed for 'Upper' is not known – and it may be remarked parenthetically that, notwithstanding the imposing two volumes of Meinertzhagen (1930), Egypt south of Cairo and on both sides of the Nile Valley remains one of the worst-documented parts of Africa – but Tregenza (1951) has since supplied evidence for the prevalence of the bird all over the mountainous eastern desert and on the Red Sea coast from July onwards. There he found its food to consist of bee-eaters, smaller migrants and also bats. Meinertzhagen (1930) included the statements, at first sight somewhat contradictory, that 'a pair bred in 1928 near Ma'adi (near Cairo)' and that 'a nest has yet to be found in Egypt'. As recently as 1954 Meinertzhagen cited no locality east of Egypt, but Vaurie (1965) included in the species' range 'Near East,* breeds in the Dead Sea depression'.

West of the Nile there are records in half a dozen widely scattered localities, mostly in extreme desert. The man who subsequently became Burmese Wingate found these falcons associated with very small rocky outcrops in the utter desolation of the Sand Sea (a huge dune-system) south of Siwa (Moreau, 1934) and from the feathers round these places it seems that their prey there consisted of small passerines. The most westerly record seems to be at Ghat, on the south-western border of Tripolitania (Heim de Balsac & Mayaud, 1962), no credence being given to the locality 'côtes de Barberie' in the original description of the bird by Temminck. The most south-westerly record is in Tchad at about 13° 45′ N, 13° 40′ E (Salvan, 1967), where on 10th June one of the birds was feeding on a hatch of 'hymenoptera' along with the swifts *A. aequatorialis* and *A. pallidus*. It had enlarged testes and was probably on its way to breed in the desert further north. In the Sudan it has been listed as 'an uncommon resident in rocky jebels in the north' (Cave & Macdonald, 1955), but it seems to be recorded with certainty only from Port Sudan, Dongola and Darfur. Actually Lynes (1924) omitted the species from his Darfur list but a male and female he collected at Kulme, about 13° 30′ N, 23° 30′ E, on 14th and 21st June were included under *F. ardosiacus* (*Ibis*, (1925): 397) and exist in the British Museum. Neither bird had enlarged gonads – from what appears below, perhaps *pace* the Tchad record, the date was too early. The Dongola record is presumably based on the BM specimen from 'Rowandab, Nubia' (an unidentifiable locality) collected on 10th September, well within the breeding season. The basis of the Port Sudan record remains uncertain, but over much of the mountainous desert north of this, between the Red Sea and the Nile, Tregenza (1951) became familiar with these birds. Of the breeding of *F. concolor* the best documentation comes from Clapham (1964) on the Dahlac Islands in the southern Red Sea off Massawa where Heuglin had found the species a hundred years earlier. Eggs (2–4) and young were in the nest around the end of August.

From the foregoing, we have evidence that the Sooty Falcon breeds in three different types of arid environment: (1) islands, (2) deeply cut, mountainous desert such as fills the area between the Nile, the Red Sea and the north-eastern Sudan, to a total area of over 100,000 square miles (compare 93,000 for the United Kingdom), (3) an area of nearly one million square miles west of the Nile, with far more widely spaced 'suitable' breeding sites in so far as rocky outcrops and precipitous faces are required. On 26th August, Booth (1967), however, found a pair with three eggs in a cairn a few feet high on the featureless 'gravel sheet', utterly devoid of vegetation, west of Kufra Oasis. He repeatedly encountered this species between about 20° and 25° E and as far south as 20° S. The falcons were mainly active at dawn and dusk, feeding on bats and on small migrants – he specifies Willow Warblers

*'Near East' is, of course, an immensely vague expression and Vaurie (pers. comm.) states that no supporting or limiting details are now recoverable. A. Zahavi (pers. comm.) supports the record for the Dead Sea and is reasonably certain that the bird occurs in Sinai, but there is no evidence that it does so much further north. Since the foregoing was written, Professor H. Mendelssohn has informed me independently that there seems no evidence for breeding in Israel outside the Dead Sea depression, with certain breeding there limited to one nest 'in the salt cliffs of Sodom'.

Phylloscopus trochilus, Whitethroats *Sylvia communis* and Subalpine Warblers *Sylvia cantillans.*

By far the greatest breeding concentration of these falcons appears to be in the southern Red Sea, where Clapham (1964) found 170 pairs with eggs or young in that part of the Dahlac Archipelago which he visited in August. Very likely most of the numerous rocky islands that litter the Red Sea, especially on the Arabian side, are occupied by these falcons – note the record by Long (1961) at 18° 59′ N, 2nd May (very early), 'about 100 miles from land'. The Dahlac falcons had been feeding on very different, much larger migrants than those eaten in the Libyan desert, primarily Blue-cheeked Bee-eaters *Merops superciliosus,* Hoopoes *Upupa epops* and *Oriolus oriolus,* in that order of abundance.

A big question is how far south and east the breeding range of the species extends and it is, I am afraid, not too much to say that the answer has been bedevilled by Meinertzhagen. In 1930 he referred to 'a pair which bred regularly in the Old Fort at Mombasa', a locality far away from the others cited, at about 4° S and in a totally different climate and environment. In 1938 Jackson reproduced this statement, but later (Meinertzhagen, 1954) it became 'in 1902 there used to be a small colony in the Old Fort'. The record is now generally disbelieved but, since no dates are given, it may all be based on wintering birds (see below). Eastwards in Somaliland the species has been cited as breeding, but according to Archer & Godman (1937) it is 'impossible to say whether it is resident or not'. This opinion has evidently been influenced by the fact that the Somaliland records are all in May and June, by which dates 'the ordinary migratory birds would have departed'. True enough; but this is far from being an 'ordinary' bird since it breeds after the summer solstice. Anyway, although Heuglin recorded the species from the 'Somali coast', of the three localities cited for specimens, the two identifiable are about 30 and 60 miles inland, and so likely to be on their way back from winter quarters.

The Gulf of Aden itself has not yielded the data on the Sooty Falcon that might have been expected. Myles North (1946) did not find it on the apparently eligible Mait Island nor during his long stay at Bandar Kassim, about 130 miles west of Cape Guardafui. (Following his regretted death his records have been lent to me for examination: he had hopefully prepared an index card for this species, but it contains no entries.) Moreover, A. Forbes-Watson in his recent careful working of Socotra and Abd-el-Kuri failed to encounter the bird (Ripley & Bond, 1966), though Jones (1946) had recorded as 'common ... to all the islands' of the Brothers group, just west of Socotra, in August, what appeared to be *F. concolor.*

On 10th November, 1936, at 4° 40′ N, 49° 20′ E, about 100 miles off the East African coast, I saw three falcons I concluded were *concolor,* which, after circling round the ship, passed on westwards (Moreau, 1938). If the identification was correct it could only point to a breeding population far to the east.

52

The last thing I would want to do is to insist on a compass bearing, but certainly the falcons approached from the side of the open Indian Ocean and this they are most unlikely to have done unless they had flown from some point east of 49° E and probably much further east, at least towards the south-eastern corner of the Arabian peninsula.

Authors' current restriction of the breeding range of the Sooty Falcon to west of the eastern shore of the Red Sea no doubt derives from the obfuscations of Meinertzhagen (1954) which it is now possible to sweep away. First, there is no good reason to doubt the August specimen from Charbar, at about 60° 30′ E, on the Mekran coast, as recorded by Ticehurst (1927). It was collected by Cumming, curator of the Quetta Museum, who tentatively identified others of this species up to 300 miles further east (*ibid.*). As for the Muscat specimen (*Ibis* (1886): 163) rejected by Meinertzhagen, the fact that its wings are cut shows that it had been in captivity and so conceivably, but in the circumstances of its time improbably, might not have been a local bird. However, H.E. Ennion (pers. comm.) during 1962–63 repeatedly saw Sooty Falcons on the coast of Oman some 250 miles in length that faces north-east past Muscat, between Sur and Sohar. Here there are long stretches of cliff 50 to 60 feet high and two islets, Fahl and Suadi, each three to four acres in extent with inaccessible cliffs of 30 to 40 feet. At Fahl Ennion observed three to four pairs on 19th June, 22 in the air at once on 22nd October; at Suadi one on 26th January, four on 31st January, six plus on 15th April and five on 26th July. Furthermore, W. Stanford (pers. comm.), reconnoitring Fahl Island from a helicopter in June 1968, observed 'at least six birds' there.

To fill in the great gap between the Red Sea on the west and the Oman and Mekran coasts in the east, one would expect Sooty Falcons to nest along the coasts of South Arabia and northern Somaliland. However, the only evidence for southern Arabia is negative: Green (1949) explicitly reported that on Masirah Island the only raptorial birds were the anomalous *Elanus caeruleus*. On the other hand we now have evidence for the Sooty Falcon in the Persian Gulf, where suitable breeding sites are probably in numbers. W. Stanford (pers. comm.) writes:

> I saw two pairs at Yas Island in June, 1968. It is a fairly large island with a rocky and precipitous centre, uninhabited but accessible [about 75 miles SSW of Abu Dhabi in the Trucial States]. It is used as an artillery and bombing range but most of this activity is concentrated on the flat plain rather than the central peaks. The falcons were very tame: they soared close to us as we sat upon the rocks and were particularly noisy at last light and indeed after dark. I was there for only about 24 hours, so could not see if they were nesting [probably too early]. I did not have time to examine either the cliffs or the east side of the Musandam Peninsula nor another rocky islet near Yas, but the former are very like those [occupied by the falcons] south of Muscat.

Ennion's records in Oman in January, cited above, show that not all Sooty Falcons migrate, but most must do so.

Of the winter quarters the most remarkable documentation is that of Rand (1936). He found large numbers in the western (drier) parts of Malagasy from 23rd November (note how this accords with the November date of my birds off the East African coast) and 6th April. In different localities he recorded 'twenty or more', 'sometimes as many as fifteen', 'common ... sometimes as many as seven perched on one tree in open marshy country where trees were scarce', 'in savanna country ... often noted perched on low ant-hills'. Twenty-three stomachs contained insect remains, mostly locusts; only one a bird. Even though *F. concolor* may not occupy more than about 100,000 square miles of Malagasy, Rand's records give an impression of numbers that are amazingly large if the breeding range were indeed limited to the Red Sea and westwards. Moreover, the British Museum possesses no less than twenty specimens collected in Malagasy. The statement that the bird has reached Mauritius (Rountree *et al.*, 1952) 400 miles east of Malagasy is, however, erroneous; the specimen concerned, which is in Cambridge, is *F. eleonorae* (C.W. Benson, pers. comm.).

Mackworth-Praed & Grant (1955) made the generalization that the Sooty Falcon is 'a regular winter visitor to eastern Africa in some numbers, as well as a resident'. The details on which this was based cannot now be recovered (Mackworth-Praed pers. comm.). The mention of 'resident' can only be based on that Mombasa record; and the evidence for wintering must have been at best tenuous since the British Museum possesses no African specimen from south of the Sudan, though its records show that it once had one (undated) from 'Abyssinia'. After the preparation of this book, however, Stresemann (1955) listed a specimen from Dar-es-Salaam on 24th March (1894), presumably in winter quarters, one from Ukerewe Island in Lake Victoria, and a third, also infuriatingly without date, from 'Mossamedes'. This last record Stresemann has asked me to correct, the specimen in fact having been collected in Mozambique by W. Peters in 1875. Jackson knew of one from Archer's Post in northern Kenya, again undated; however, there is now evidence for both wintering and considerable passage in Kenya. On the one hand, C.W. Benson tells me that the National Museum at Nairobi possesses specimens from Naivasha 18th December, Sabaki River 20th November and Nairobi 21st January. On the other hand, I.S.C. Parker has recently found it to be 'a regular passage migrant in some numbers' through eastern Kenya and that on the lower Athi River it eats Queleas (L.H. Brown, pers. comm., who has seen Sooty Falcons also at Lake Nakuru). Eighteen hundred miles to the south, Clancey (1969) has just reported three records in Natal. From the standard works and subsequent information on the birds of Malawi, Zambia and Rhodesia the Sooty Falcon has never been recognised in that great block of territory, part of which it must surely at least traverse.

From all the foregoing we have highly sporadic but inexpugnable evidence that the Sooty Falcon winters in eastern Africa at least from the equator to 30° S, perhaps inland to Lake Victoria. As a breeding bird the Sooty

Falcon should be looked for from the Dead Sea and the eastern shore of the Red Sea to Baluchistan and as a wintering bird from Kenya to Natal.

Evidently the Sooty Falcon must be much more numerous than Eleonora's, which is reliably estimated at 2,500 pairs ± 500 (Walter 1968), so that 10,000 of them would exist each autumn. Stresemann (1968) has calculated that Eleonora's should altogether take the equivalent of 13 million birds of the size of a Nightingale out of the autumn migrants. In terms of biomass the Sooty Falcons would take a far heavier toll, though not correspondingly in terms of individuals, because the prey species of the southern breeding birds are much bigger.

Summary

Sooty Falcons breed in late summer from about 25° N, 10° E in the Libyan Desert, through the neighbourhood of Cairo and east into Palestine, south to the Gulf of Aden, the northern Sudan and perhaps northern Tchad. There are good reasons for supposing that they breed also 1,000–1,500 miles further east in the Persian Gulf, on the coast of Oman and along the Mekran, so that the bird should be looked for along the south coast of Arabia, indeed in its interior also. Sooty Falcons feed on much bigger birds, e.g. bee-eaters, in the south of their range than in the north, where warblers bulk large, and in sum the Sooty Falcon population must take much heavier toll than do Eleanora's. In winter they are common in Malagasy but also occur from Kenya to Natal.

References

Booth, B.D.Mcd. (1961). Breeding of the Sooty Falcon in the Libyan Desert, *Ibis*, 103a: 129–31.

Cave, F.O. & Macdonald, J.D. (1955). *Birds of the Sudan*, Edinburgh & London: Oliver & Boyd.

Clancey, P.A. (1969). *Falco concolor* Temminck in South Africa, *Bull. Brit. Orn. Cl.* 89: 10–11.

Clapman, C.S. (1964). The birds of the Dahlac archipelago, *Ibis* 106: 376–88.

Goodwin, D. (1949). Notes on the migration of birds of prey over Suez, *Ibis* 91: 59–63.

Green, C. (1949). The Black-shouldered Kite in Masira (Oman), *Ibis* 91: 459–64.

Heim de Balsac, H. and Mayaud, N. (1962). *Les oiseaux du nord-ouest de l'Afrique*, Paris: Lechevalier.

Jackson, F.J. and Sclater, W.L. (1938). *The birds of Kenya Colony and the Uganda Protectorate*, London: Gurney & Jackson.

Jones, R.B. (1946). An account of a visit to the Brothers (Jebel Teir) Islands in the Gulf of Aden, *Ibis* 88: 228–32.

Long, R.C. (1961). Some land birds noted at sea, *Ibis* 103a: 131–33.

Lynes, H. (1924–5). On the birds of north and central Darfur, *Ibis* (11) 6: 399–446, 648–710; (12) 1: 71–131, 344–416, 541–90, 757–97.

Mackworth-Praed, C.W. and Grant, C.H.B. (1952). *Birds of eastern and north-eastern Africa*, London: Longmans.

Meinertzhagen, R. (1930). *Nicoll's birds of Egypt*, vol. 2, London: Hugh Rees.

—— (1954). *Birds of Arabia*. Edinburgh & London: Oliver & Boyd.

Moreau, R.E. (1934). A contribution to the ornithology of the Libyan desert, *Ibis* (13) 5: 595–632.

—— (1938). Bird migration over the north-western part of the Indian Ocean, the Red Sea and the Mediterranean, *Proc. Zool. Soc. London*, 108: 1–26.

Nicoll, M.J. (1919). *Handlist of the birds of Egypt*, Cairo: Govt. Press.

North, M. (1946). Mait Island – a bird rock in the Gulf of Aden, *Ibis* 88: 478–501.

Rand, A.L. (1936). The distribution and habits of Madagascar birds, *Bull. Am. Mus. Nat. Hist.* 72: 143–499.

Ripley, S.D. and Bond, G.M. (1966). The birds of Socotra and Abd-el-Kuri, *Smithson. Misc. Coll.* 151 (7).

Rountree, F.R.G. *et al.* (1952). Catalogue of the birds of Mauritius, *Mauritius Inst. Bull.* 3: 155–217.

Salvan, J. (1968). Contribution à l'étude des oiseaux du Tchad (Part), *Oiseau* 38: 53–85.

Stresemann, E. (1955). Das Jugendkleid von *Falco concolor*, *J. Orn.* 96: 122–23.

—— (1968). Der Eingriff der Eleonorenfalken in der herbstliche Vogelzug, *J. Orn.* 109: 472–74.

Ticehurst, C.B. (1927). The birds of British Baluchistan. *J. Bombay Nat. Hist. Soc.* 32: 71.

Tregenza, L.A. (1951). Observations on the birds of the SE desert of Egypt, *Zool. Soc. Egypt Bull.* 11: 1–18.

Vaurie, C. (1965). *The birds of the Palearctic fauna*, London: Witherby.

Walter, H. (1968). Zu Abhängigkeit der Eleonorenfalken (*Falco eleonorae*) vom mediterranan Vogelzug, *J. Orn.* 109: 323–65.

Ecology and behaviour

These subjects did not feature prominently in the early volumes of the *Bulletin*, nor in those of most other ornithological journals of that time. Nevertheless, there were some interesting items, and the Cuckoo controversy (in particular, how it laid its eggs) was a conspicuous feature of the *Bulletin* in the 1910s and 1920s, causing heated discussion at the Club's meetings. Papers on ecology and behaviour became more prominent from the 1950s onwards, and a small but diverse selection is included here.

Goodfellow on the behaviour of birds of paradise

From the report on the Club's meeting on 18 November 1908.

Mr Walter Goodfellow gave the following interesting account of his recent expedition to British New Guinea to procure living examples of Birds of Paradise, and added some valuable notes on the habits of the various species met with during his travels:

The wet season in British New Guinea lasts from November till May on the western side of the main Owen Stanley range. During this period it is dry on the eastern side, and many species of birds appear to migrate there at this season, while others seem to do so partially. At any rate, they were scarce on the western slopes during the rains, but, after the change of the monsoon, they became very numerous. This applies especially to many species of Pigeons. All the Birds of Paradise appear to moult during the rainy season, and the species frequenting the lower altitudes are the first to do so. For instance, in January *Paradisea raggiana* was in full moult, whereas *Paradisornis rudolphi* had not commenced to change its plumage. *Charmosyna stellae* and

Charmosynopsis pulchella, two species of Lories which are common at 3,000 ft and upwards, were nesting during January and February, and began to moult in April.

Paradisea raggiana and *Ptilorhis intercedens* were not met with above an altitude of 3,000 ft; beyond that *Parotia lawesi* and *Lophorina minor* were found at 6,000 ft, the latter species ascending still higher. *Diphyllodes hunsteini* was common at 3,000 ft, but specimens were also procured at 5,000 ft. Of *Loria mariae* three specimens only were seen at 5,000 ft, while *Drepanornis cervinicauda* was fairly numerous, although not often seen, at from 3,000 to 5,000 ft.

Paradisornis rudolphi, Epimachus meyeri, and *Astrapia stephaniae* were not seen below an altitude of 6,000 ft. All three species were rare in the Moroko regions, as they have been relentlessly persecuted there for many years past. The first bird shot on the expedition was a female of *P. rudolphi*; two males were also seen, one at the same time and the other on a subsequent occasion. These birds appear to be very local, and the natives say (and it seems to be true) that they frequent the vicinity of rocky cliffs. At one place on the coast, natives from the interior were seen who had evidently come from a region where these birds were very numerous. They had come down to trade the blue plumes with the coast natives, and had the complete side-plumes fixed to strings in yard lengths. The same people also had great numbers of the complete crests of *Amblyornis subalaris* and *A. inornata*, which, like the two long feathers of *Charmosyna stellae*, are in great demand on the coast for making 'dancing' ornaments. *P. rudolphi* has a remarkably agreeable call for a Bird of Paradise, although it is unmistakably the note of a bird of that family. It keeps to the high trees, but, according to the natives, is easily snared as it comes low down to dance.

Only one example of *Epimachus meyeri* was seen. The notes of this species are most remarkable, and consist of a loud, sharply emitted, blowing noise, and a sound very much like the rattle of a kettledrum. The bird seen had a rapid flight and Creeper-like habits, and alighted directly on the perpendicular trunk of a tree.

Only one example of *Astrapia stephaniae* was procured and three examples of *Loria mariae*. The legs and feet of the last named species are holly-green in the male, but less bright in the female. In life the gape of this bird is very remarkable, for it projects for a considerable distance beyond the sides of the face, and is of a primrose-yellow colour. The inside of the throat is pink, so when the mouth is open it has the appearance of a *Gloxinia*.

Drepanornis cervinicauda subsists chiefly on insects, and was seen clinging to the ends of rotten branches and probing the holes with its long bill. It frequents the lower forest growth, and was sometimes seen flying a short distance above the ground. A living example of this bird was brought home and has become very tame. The food is thrown up and jerked to the back of the throat, after the manner of a Toucan.

Lophorina minor appears to nest in April, as a *pair* of birds of that species were constantly seen carrying nesting materials past the camp, but the nature of the mountains did not permit of my following them up to their nesting-site. These birds have no regular dancing places, but go through their display high up in the forest trees, and hanging, for choice, from a vine, where the sunlight strikes on them, form a wonderful picture. The discordant noise made during their gymnastics could be heard at a very long distance. This species appears to be chiefly insectivorous, and a living example, which was brought home, is still doing well.

Parotia lawesi dances very low down near the ground, generally on vines or rattans which trail along the floor of the forest. During the display curious snake-like movements are made with the neck. At one dancing place twenty or thirty birds were seen at one time during the month of May.

Diphyllodes hunsteini also dances low down, choosing a slender tree about 7 ft high from which every leaf is stripped. The ground too, for a considerable circumference around, is kept carefully cleared of all leaves and debris. Each dancing place appears to be used by one pair of birds only. Although this is a numerous species, it is the one that is least seen, as the birds keep entirely to the thick cover. They have an exceedingly loud and harsh call, which is often heard.

Paradisea raggiana, like the other members of this genus, chooses a high tree for its display. The dancing-season does not commence much before April, and the birds are then to be found there regularly for a short time at 7 a.m., and again for a considerable time at 2 p.m. One habit of this bird has not been noted in the other species – a backward, jerky movement along the branches; also, perhaps, the curious way in which the female birds thread in and out along the branch under the depressed tail of the male, reminding one of the 'ladies' chain' in a quadrille. Nesting commences in April, and the male bird takes no part whatever either in building the nest or in rearing the young. In the beginning of May a nest was found in the course of construction in the fork of a branch about 10 ft above the ground, on the edge of a small inhabited clearing. It was a very flimsy structure composed of fibre and dead leaves, but twice during the period of incubation the female bird entwined a fresh green creeper negligently about the nest and the fork in which it was placed. Only one egg was laid, and incubation appeared to last eighteen days. The young bird was eventually taken and hand-reared and, together with its mother, was brought to England, where both are now living. It proved to be a male, and shows the ochre-coloured bar, which is characteristic of the young of that sex, beneath what will later on be the green throat. The throat and nasal region (which are both green in the adult male) remained entirely bare until the young bird was nearly two months old, although the rest of the body was fully feathered.

At the end of May another nest was found in a similar situation to that already mentioned, but it was placed still lower down. In this case also only one egg was laid and after it had hatched the young bird was taken and brought up by hand. The mother was also captured, and both are now in England. This young one also turned out to be a male.

On June the 9th a nest of *Ptilorhis intercedens* was found in a small breadfruit tree. It was placed about 12 ft from the ground, and the tree stood in the centre of an overgrown clearing. As a move was being made back to port, the nest and two eggs were taken and the female bird was captured; but two days after it arrived in England it escaped in the country near to Tunbridge Wells.* This nest, together with those of *Paradisea raggiana*, was found in the Moroka Mountains, at an altitude of 2,000 ft.

Three living pairs of the rifle-bird, *P. intercedens*, were brought home alive; also pairs of *P. raggiana*; *P. lawesi*, with the males in full plumage; and many pairs of *D. hunsteini*, all the males being in adult plumage.

* * *

Walter Goodfellow was a remarkably perceptive observer, who allowed few details to escape his attention. He did not hesitate to make hypotheses based on his observations. In some instances these hypotheses proved faulty (based on too few data), but in other cases they were perfectly correct. Considering the difficulty of working in British New Guinea in 1908, Goodfellow's thoughts are startlingly 'modern'.

Goodfellow's surmise that some resident bird species migrate within New Guinea in order to move from local wet to dry conditions sounded farfetched even a decade ago, but finally some data are coming to light that may support this notion. One population of the alpine-dwelling Macgregor's Bird of Paradise (*Macgregoria pulchra*) is known to 'disappear' for months from a regular breeding site. To where do these birds migrate? Flocks of Papuan Mountain Pigeons and several species of lorikeets have been seen flying at high altitudes, in apparent migration. The details of these local migrations in New Guinea remain a mystery.

Goodfellow's notes on the birds of paradise of the Owen Stanley Range still today stand as accurate reports on the birds' seasonality and distributional ecology. Goodfellow notes the elevational displacement of paradisaeid species that was further illuminated by Professor Jared Diamond in the 1960s and 1970s.

Goodfellow's notes on he display of '*Lophorina minor*' (the Superb Bird of

---

*I have just heard from Mr Goodfellow that the female Rifle-bird has been recaptured alive. It escaped on September the 6th and remained at liberty till November the 18th, when one evening it flew against the window of the rectory at Langton, being attracted by the lights. During that period many of the nights were wet and cold, and recently as many as 17° of frost have been registered; but the bird, though somewhat thin, was well and in good plumage. This shows what Birds of Paradise can stand, and when provided with good food they could no doubt endure even greater cold with impunity. Ed.

Paradise, now treated as *L. superba*) have now been updated by Clifford and Dawn Frith, who have shown that the male displays near the ground on a fallen log.

Most remarkable is that Goodfellow worked to elaborate a conservation plan for birds of paradise in the days when such a concept passed through few ornithologists' heads.

BRUCE M. BEEHLER

Display of snipe and woodcock

Dr P.H. (later Sir Philip) Manson-Bahr, a leading authority on tropical medicine, had a long-standing interest in the anatomical specialisations of waders and their associated displays. The first of the following extracts was communicated to the Club in 1912; the second, shorter extract in 1931. Some of the questions with which he deals are still not fully resolved; for instance, it is still not known for certain whether (or which of) the sounds made during the Jack Snipe's display-flight are vocal or mechanical (*Birds of the Western Palearctic*, vol. 3: 406–8). The method by which snipe, woodcock and other waders open the bill-tip when probing for food has now been studied in more detail by P.J.K. Burton (*Feeding and the Feeding Apparatus in Waders*, 1974), one of the few British ornithologists to have carried on the tradition of research into the functional morphology of birds, of which Manson-Bahr was an outstanding pioneer.

In his obituary of Manson-Bahr in *The Ibis* (109 (1967): 447–8), Landsborough Thomson recalled the occasion when he gave the talk from which the second extract is taken.

> In 1931, Manson-Bahr repeated his demonstration [of the way in which the Common Snipe makes its drumming sound, earlier given before the Zoological Society] for the edification of the British Ornithologists' Club. With his usual accomplished showmanship, he made the room in Pagani's Restaurant resound to the drumming of the Snipe, produced by whirling round, on the end of a string, a cork in which the two effective rectrices had been inserted at the proper angle.

From the report on the Club's meeting on 14 February 1912.

Dr P.H. Bahr [on his marriage he changed his name to Manson-Bahr] made the following remarks:

The interesting discoveries of Mr Pycraft [who had given a talk of the syrinx of the Jack Snipe] have added another to the list of specialised structures for which the *Scolopacinae* are remarkable. To my mind, the fact that the syrinx of the Jack Snipe (*Limnocryptes gallinula*) is provided with an intercalary bar of cartilage, as Mr Pycraft has already pointed out, explains a great deal.

During the course of a number of experiments which I published in 1907, I experimented with both the primary wing-feathers and the rectrices of this Snipe, but was not able to produce any characteristic sound with either of them. Wolley has stated, and the accuracy of his statements are proverbial, that in Lapland this Snipe while soaring, at a great height over its breeding-grounds, makes a sound comparable to that of a horse galloping over a hard road. We have now, in view of Mr Pycraft's interesting discovery, some reason to believe that the origin of this sound is vocal.

We have records, made by such excellent observers as Prof. Collett, that the Great Snipe (*Gallinago major*), though an allied species, has an entirely different nuptial display. The males, it is said, meet together on common ground, and there, in much the same manner as the Blackcock, display before the hens. The chief point about this display is that the tail is spread out like a fan and moved up and down, as if the bird was anxious to do something with its tail, but did not quite know how to set about it. In this wise the pure white outer tail-feathers are shown to the admiring gaze of the opposite sex. In view of the fact that the performance takes place on the ground and that there are no specialised structures, in either the wing or the tail, which could possibly serve as musical instruments, we are forced to conclude that the sounds made by this Snipe, too, must be vocal in origin. It has always seemed to me a remarkable thing that some of the *Scolopacinae* should have such specialised musical instruments in their wings or tail, and that others, although in form and anatomical features apparently so closely allied, should have to depend upon their vocal organs for giving vent to their feelings during the breeding season.

The European Common Snipe possesses definite specialised feathers in the tail which produce sound. These feathers differ from others in the tail not only in their gross, but also in their minute structure, and can be recognised at a glance. That they are definite musical instruments there can be no doubt, as with them the identical well-known 'bleat' can be reproduced by actual experiment, as was pointed out by Meves in 1856. The radii of the inner web of these feathers are firm and stiff and fashioned as the strings of a harp. To keep them taut during the performance and to ensure their vibration when acted on by the aerial resistance, a band of specialised muscle-fibres runs to each of these feathers, so that when the tail is spread they project beyond the others. These facts are now well known; but what is not so well known or appreciated is the fact that in the different geographical races and species of Snipe these specialised structures have become more and more specialised.

In Wilson's Snipe (*G. delicata*) not only are there four of these musical instruments in the tail, but in them specialisation has gone still further, and the inner web of the feather has become attenuated; while in two other South American species (*G. nobilis* and *G. frenata*) the number of specialised feathers has increased and the attenuation has become more marked.

In the African species (*G. aequatorialis*), and more so in the Eastern Asiatic species (*G. solitaria, G. australis,* and *G. megala*), this specialisation has become still more marked, and reaches its climax in the Pin-tailed Snipe (*G. stenura*). In that species there are a variable number of feathers (generally sixteen) in the tail, which have become so attenuated that the shaft has become more or less bereft of all rami and radii. Thus, being shorn of their strings, so to speak, only the frame remains.

From Taczanowski and Alan Owston we have good accounts of the breeding habits of *G. solitaria* and *G. australis*; and they perform in much the same manner as the Common Snipe, but the 'bleat' is of a higher pitch and is much louder.

Of the breeding-habits of *G. stenura* little appears to be known. Buturlin says it spreads its tail in the same manner, but that in rushing through the air no sound is produced.* This statement is confirmed by my experiments, in which I was unable to produce any sounds with these feathers. So in this species specialisation has proceeded to such an extent as to defeat the object for which these feathers were created.

When we turn to the Woodcocks, we find that both the European and American species have remarkable nuptial displays.

Of the European species (*Scolopax rusticola*) I will not say much. This bird does not possess specialised feathers in either its wings or tail, and, to my mind, the sounds it emits are undoubtedly vocal.

But in the American species (*Philohela minor*) there is a totally different condition of affairs. This bird has a most elaborate and characteristic nuptial flight, which has been well, and poetically, described by Mr Frank Chapman.

In the middle of last March I was so fortunate as to be present at such a performance. The sun had already set an hour, when we repaired to an open piece of ground, amongst some woods, not ten miles from New York City. The Woodcocks could be heard making their curious nuptial call − a sort of a sneeze, quite indescribable in words − in the vicinity, when suddenly, with a whirr of wings, one of the birds beat its way heavenwards. It was much too dark to see what was taking place, but evidently, after reaching the zenith of its flight, the bird began to circle round, uttering the while the sweetest of all

---

*Prjevalsky has published an interesting article on this species under the name *Gallinago heter-ocera* [*cf.* Rowley's *Orn. Misc.,* iii, p. 91 (1878)]. He says that the Pintailed Snipe dashes downwards with great noise, which he believed was produced by the tail-feathers. Ed.

musical cadences, probably vocally produced. Then followed a swish of a high-pitched sound, remarkably like certain sounds in the 'drumming' of our Snipe, and undoubtedly produced by feather vibration. To the accompaniment of this music the Woodcock returned to earth and to its mate. The whole performance lasted well over a minute.

On seeking an explanation of this finale, we find that the three outer primaries in the wing of this Woodcock are shorter, stiffer, and more attenuated than the others. I feel sure that in these specialised feathers – and, if specialised, they must have some special function to perform – will be found the explanation of part at least of the nuptial display of this bird.

I take it that these varied and highly interesting habits of the *Scolopacinae* during the breeding-season are but the development of the less elaborate display of other Waders, such as the Redshank and the Black-tailed Godwit.

I can imagine no more fascinating pursuit than the accurate study of the habits of these different species on the spot. Such a study is urgently required.

There is one more peculiarity of this family which I should like to touch upon before closing. I refer to the remarkable power possessed by these long-billed birds of elevating the premaxilla apart from the maxilla. The object of this movement is obviously to assist the bird to catch and hold earthworms while its beak is immersed up to the nostrils in mud. The mechanism by which this movement is performed is said to be due to the action of the endo-tympanic muscle, a very insignificant slip to overcome such a great amount of resistance.

In examining freshly killed Snipe and Woodcock, I have been surprised to find the ease with which this movement of the premaxilla can be performed, merely by pressing on the angle of the mandible, in this way imitating the action of the masseter muscle. By these means the quadrate bones are tilted forward, themselves in turn imparting the movement to the palatine processes of the maxilla and thus forcing the premaxilla upwards.

To my mind this is a simple explanation of the manner in which these birds catch their elusive prey beneath ground. By merely pressing the upper and lower mandibles tighter together the tip of the beak opens and the desired result is obtained.

The position of the eye and that of the extensor auditory meatus in these birds add to an already long list of admirable adaptations for which the subfamily *Scolopacinae* is so remarkable.

From a later paper by P.H. Manson-Bahr (1931, vol. 51: 96–7).

The Jack-Snipe has twelve tail-feathers, all Woodcock-like, and none specialised. On examination and experiment none produce a musical note whatever. It is very doubtful now whether Wolley's famous description of this bird on June 17, 1853, is correct (Newton, *Ootheca Wolleyana*, vol. ii, pp. 252–3), who compared it to the 'cantering of a horse in the distance on a hard hollow ground; it comes in fours, with a similar cadence and a like clear, yet hollow sound.' Russow (Hartert, *Vögel Paläark. Fauna*, 1912–21, ii, p. 1671) believes that the noise is made with the beak, like the '*Knebbern*' of *C. media*. He says (*loc. cit.*): 'It circles in the air, and whilst flying makes a sound like a wagon-wheel out of which a piece of tyre is missing [Estonian local name for this bird signifies "a broken wheel"]. The female, *per contra*, is said to make a clicking noise like that of the death-watch beetle.' The latest observer is Chislett (*British Birds*, xxi, 1927, pp. 2–3), who thinks that Wolley's description is only partially correct. It is a short muffled sound, curiously distant, yet near, at one moment almost clear, then suddenly confused. Sometimes the bird could be seen patrolling high above, while at the other times no bird was visible, and the sound seemed to emanate from the ground.

The evolution of clutch size

When Stuart Baker gave the following talk, in 1916, he adumbrated ideas that were well in advance of their time. It was more than thirty years later that David Lack (*Ibis* 89 (1947): 302–52; 90 (1948): 24–45) set clutch size in birds in an evolutionary context, and proposed ideas that were to stimulate numerous ecological studies in the following decades. In 1916 the topic was thought of as 'variations in' rather than 'the evolution of' clutch size; but while not putting his arguments in modern evolutionary terms, Stuart Baker convincingly argued for the fundamental role played by availability of food, and suggested the basic reason for variations in clutch size with latitude.

From the report on the Club's meeting on 10 January 1917.

Mr E.C. Stuart Baker exhibited some clutches of eggs of the Common Sand-piper, *Tringa hypoleuca*, containing an abnormal number of eggs – in two clutches six and in two others five. Together with these the Rev. F.C.R. Jourdain exhibited two other clutches containing five eggs.

In a discussion which arose upon this exhibition, in which several members took part, the exhibitor stated that all six of the clutches shown, together with two others which had passed through his hands, had been collected in Kashmir, either in the vicinity of Gulmurg and Gandarbal or close to Srinagar, the chief town of that state. In many parts of Kashmir the Common Sandpiper bred in great numbers, and these abnormally large

65

clutches probably only represented about one per cent of those taken or seen *in situ* during the last twenty-five years.

He went on to remark:

> The causes which govern the variations which occur in the number of eggs normally laid in a single clutch by species, genera, and families of birds are very complex, and no less complex are the laws which cause abnormal increases or decreases.
>
> Underlying the whole we have, of course, Nature's dominant law that reproduction must be on a scale sufficiently large to ensure continuation of the species, and counterbalancing this the never-ending competition between individuals, between species, and between families.
>
> But Nature's motive power to all this is *food*, and undoubtedly *food* decides what number of eggs a bird shall lay, though food is itself dependent on many conflicting conditions – both climatic and geographical. In some cases these conditions are more or less permanent, in others they are temporary only; in some cases they obtain over vast areas and in many they are purely local.
>
> To touch even the outskirts of this vast question is not possible in the time at our disposal, but there are perhaps one or two rules, well known to those who study oology in its wider branches, which are fairly consistent in their working and to which I would briefly refer. The first of these rules is the very constant one, that birds in high temperate latitudes lay more eggs in a clutch than they do in tropical countries. At first sight one might urge that this appears to be a direct contradiction of the theory that food is the principal factor governing the production of eggs, for food is surely more plentiful on the average in tropical than in temperate climates. A little thought, however, shows that the contrary is obvious.
>
> It is true that food *is* more plentiful on an average throughout the year in tropical and semitropical countries, but this plenty is found more or less at all times and seasons, and the energy which impels procreation is never in danger of complete exhaustion, whilst at the same time it never reaches the concentrated height it does in countries in which, for a great part of the year, continued effort is needed for self-support, so that there is no surplus energy available for the production and bringing up of a family.
>
> In the Arctic Circle and countries adjacent we have a short, hot summer, during which insect and certain forms of vegetable life are most extraordinarily abundant; birds feed freely and with little exertion, and attain a super-vitalized condition, with the contingent result that we have bigger clutches of eggs laid by them than are laid by individuals of the same species in more temperate countries. But we must remember this also: if we have larger clutches, due to the short fevered summer, we also have fewer clutches laid by the same female, for, once the season is fairly advanced, there is not much chance of her finding time to lay a second. First clutches which are destroyed can often never be replaced; therefore Nature demands larger clutches to balance the limitation in the breeding-season.
>
> When we get into tropical countries we find the reverse process is in existence. The breeding season is of much greater length, and many birds breed off and on practically throughout the year. Numerically large clutches are unnecessary, for if they are destroyed they can be replaced, and even if the second is lost, yet a third is possible, for food in plenty is obtainable and no excessive exhaustion is entailed in procuring it.
>
> But though in the tropics this rule of small clutches holds good, yet in such

countries local conditions cause local and temporary variations far more marked than in the higher latitudes. Thus a long drought may dry up marshes and rivers in the vicinity of which water-birds normally breed in thousands. With no water there are no fish, the birds are underfed, poor in vitality, and with no surplus energy. In consequence, they either do not breed at all or make a short migration to some adjacent locality in which an abundance of food shall once more create an excess vitality with the corresponding desire for procreation.

So, too, in some tropical countries elevation is a very potential factor in determining how many eggs shall be laid. Indeed high elevation takes the place of high latitudes, and similarity of climatic conditions produce similar effects. Thus in the higher elevations of the Himalayas we find Thrushes, Flycatchers, Accentors, etc., laying nearly as many eggs as they do in northern Europe, though not nearly as many as they do in the extreme north. On the other hand, in southern India the representatives of these same birds frequently lay only two eggs instead of four or five, as in other parts of the world.

Then, too, other factors which are connected with food create temporary and local disturbances which may cause an increase in the number of eggs laid by one species and yet have the contrary effect in others. Thus in north-west India a plague of locusts will mean that all the Raptores which prey thereon will breed with great freedom, whilst those birds whose food is destroyed by these same locusts will be weak and anaemic, and breed less freely and successfully than in normal years. So, too, an unusual flood will bring water-birds an abundance of food and will entice birds to breed which never normally did so in the district so flooded, whilst those birds which breed in the grasslands of ordinary years are prevented from breeding at all.

From the report on the Club's meeting on 14 February 1917.

Regarding the subject of abnormal clutches of eggs discussed at the last meeting, the Chairman read the following extract from a letter from Sir T. Digby Piggott:

I read with much interest the remarks of Mr Stuart Baker on the abnormally large clutches of Sandpipers' eggs he exhibited. In confirmation of his conclusions that great abundance of food is the cause of increase in number of eggs in the clutch, I think it may interest the members of the BOC to be reminded that during the plague of voles in 1891–2 the Short-eared Owls which congregated in large numbers in the plague centres laid very largely increased clutches of eggs. If I recollect rightly, the normal clutch consists of from four to six* eggs, while during the plague eight to ten eggs were common in Dumfriesshire, and many considerably larger were reported.

The following questions, put at Sir Herbert Maxwell's committee, go to prove this:

Question 25 put to a shepherd: 'How many eggs does each Owl lay?'

*Four to eight, according to *Birds of the Western Palearctic*, vol. 4: 599.

Answer: 'From nine to thirteen. There were five pairs of Owls with me (i.e. on my beat), and they have reared about 50 young ones. These five had from eight to thirteen eggs, and two are sitting for the second time.'

The same question to another witness. Answer: 'As many as ten to twelve were frequently reported, and in most instances the birds are now sitting or rearing a second brood.'

Two or three Members present stated that they had known of clutches of from eight to ten eggs in normal years in the Orkneys.

The severe winter of 1916–17

This was one of the worst winters of the century. No formal inquiry was launched (which would hardly have been possible in the middle of the war), but the reports summarised in the *Bulletin* give a useful, if not quantitative, assessment of its effect on bird populations.

From the report on the Club's meeting on 14 February 1917, when the thaw had just begun.

Dr Ernst Hartert asked if any members present had made observations about the effect of the severe frost on bird life. Near Tring many birds had suffered considerably when the ground became frozen and they could not get their natural food. The Redwings seemed to have all perished, and many Song-thrushes, Fieldfares, Blackbirds, and Mistle-thrushes had been found dead. Also a number of Starlings had been picked up, though the majority of the latter seemed to have survived. In all cases it was, of course, not the cold (as the public seemed to believe very often), but the want of food that killed these birds. They were nearly all emaciated.

Mr P.F. Bunyard said that he had heard of several Kingfishers being captured by hand in Surrey as a result of balls of ice being formed on their feet.

Mr Carruthers Gould said that during the great frost he walked over the fields between East Molesey and Esher in order to observe the effect of the cold upon bird life. He picked up a dead Heron, which appeared to have been starved and showed no sign of injury. In a ditch overhung by bushes and not quite frozen over he flushed a Greater Spotted Woodpecker and Kingfisher. The Redwings and Fieldfares had come in close to the cottages and fed upon the scraps thrown out by the cottagers, and picked over the horse-droppings in the road.

The same Member stated that, as a result of the abnormally cold weather, Lapwings were offered in Leadenball Market at 3d each, but they were all in very poor condition, and he had never seen so many Blackbirds, Thrushes, Redwings, and Fieldfares offered for sale in the market.

Mr H.B. Booth said that in his opinion many birds had some fore-knowledge of approaching severe weather. In the dales of West Yorkshire this was most noticeable immediately before a sudden and sharp spell of frost and snow, particularly towards the end of the year when the majority of certain species hurriedly left the neighbourhood, presumably for the coast. The species affected were chiefly Song-thrushes, Skylarks, and Meadow-pipits, but a sudden decrease was noticeable in several other species. These were facts proved by actual observation and not merely superstitious myths of the country people, though it was noticeable that such superstition at times seemed to be founded on fact. Thus on December 13th last a flock of about twenty Wild Geese, probably Pink-footed, settled in a certain large field in broad daylight, a very rare occurrence, although it is not unusual for Geese to fly over this particular district. The local farmers shook their heads and prophesied very bad weather, a forecast which proved to be only too true, the recent severe weather having been the worst for twenty-two years.

The birds had had a very bad time in West Yorkshire, more especially the Redwings. Red Grouse had been driven from the moors and were in large flocks quite close to the villages in the dales. Lapwings and Golden Plovers had disappeared from the low-lying fields near the river, where large flocks usually spend the winter; Wood-pigeons and Stock-doves had largely, though not entirely, left the district.

On February 11th, which might be considered as the climax of the frost, and just before the thaw commenced, about sixty frozen-out Mallard were seen in the middle of a large field, and all the Snipe and most of the small birds in the neighbourhood appeared to have congregated on the Ilkley sewage-works, regaling themselves on the offal in the sewage and on the still unfrozen sludge.

From the report on the Club's meeting on 14 November 1917.

Mr P.F. Bunyard read the following report on the effect of the severe and prolonged winter of 1916–17 on our resident birds:

At the June meeting of the BOC, when this subject was discussed, it was too early to form any concrete opinion as to those species which had had their ranks so alarmingly thinned out by the severe frosts, and those which had survived in fair numbers.

My notes include reports from numerous field observers, and no less than twenty-three of our largest fruit-growers. They include my own personal observations and are from the counties of Kent, Surrey, and Middlesex, with the exception of those on the Crossbill, Wood-lark, and Cirl Bunting, and were made before this year's broods could have had any material effect on numbers.

The Crossbill I am pleased to be able to report bred in increasing numbers, and no doubt these hardy birds, being able to obtain their food in the usual manner from the seeds of the Scotch pine, were better able to stand the severity of the weather. On the other hand, another typical Suffolk bird, the Wood-lark, has, I fear, been almost exterminated, and no nests were located where they were formerly plentiful. The Cirl Bunting was entirely absent from its usual haunts in Hampshire.

From an ornithological point of view, I consider the apparent extermination of the Dartford Warbler the most serious loss we have sustained. I have purposely made the proviso *apparently* because, from a very long experience with these birds, I am convinced that it would be impossible, owing to their very seclusive and illusive habits, to say that there were no birds left, though I failed to hear or see a single bird after repeated visits to their strongholds, some of which were made with the express object of verifying my own notes, and when the birds should have been most in evidence, i.e. when they had young. I may mention that previous to 1915 I had nearly forty pairs of these interesting birds under observation. I am of the opinion that they had then only just regained their status of the period before the severe winter of 1880–81, and that is also the opinion of a keeper who lives on the estate, and who has known the birds for fifty years.

From an economic point of view, the most serious loss has been that of the Tits. The eggs of the Winter Moth, etc., which form an important part of the food of these birds, remained untouched by the frosts, and many fruit-trees were stripped of their bloom and foliage by the larvae of this pest. Many of the large growers, thinking that the winter had rendered the eggs of this moth infertile, did not band their trees as usual, some unfortunately being unable to find sufficient labour for this process, with the disastrous results mentioned. The considerable thinning out of the Bullfinch, previously far too numerous, will no doubt help to balance Nature's account.

Other species, including those mentioned, I have tabulated as follows:

Increase	Normal	Decrease
Carrion Crow	Jackdaw	Reed-bunting
Starling	Rook	Skylark
Crossbill	Magpie	Meadow-pipit
Sparrow-hawk	Jay	Great Tit
Kestrel	Goldfinch	Green Woodpecker
Ring-dove	House-sparrow	Great Spotted
	Yellow Hammer	Woodpecker
	Barn Owl	Kingfisher

Tawny Owl	Teal	
Mallard	Shoveler	
Redshank	Heron	
Long-eared Owl	Woodcock	
	Snipe	
	Ringed Plover	
	Black-headed Gull	
	Little Grebe	
	Moorhen	
	Red-legged Partridge	

Totals: 6	12	17

Considerable decrease	*Almost exterminated*	*Exterminated*
Greenfinch	Tree-creeper	(apparently)
Hawfinch	Goldcrest	Wood-lark
Chaffinch	Long-tailed tit	Dartford Warbler
Linnet	Stonechat	
Redpoll	Hedge-sparrow	
Bullfinch	Lesser Spotted	
Cirl Bunting	Woodpecker	
Pied Wagtail		
Grey Wagtail		
Nuthatch		
Coal Tit		
Marsh-tit		
Blue Tit		
Missel-thrush		
Song-thrush		
Blackbird		
Redbreast		
Wren		
Lapwing		
Great Crested Grebe		
Coot		
Totals: 21	**6**	**2**

Out of 64 species enumerated I find 46 show a decrease. The Carrion Crow, Kestrel, and Sparrow Hawk, have certainly increased owing to the fact that many estates have been without keepers during the war, a distinct gain to ornithology.

Many of my fruit-growing friends report an increase of birds during the ripening of fruit, which must be attributed to this year's broods, though they were never present in sufficient numbers to be troublesome and the usual methods of destroying did not become necessary.

Quite casual observers have been struck by the scarcity of birds. My old and valued friend and one of our best all-round county naturalists, Mr C.F. Stedman, of Ashford, Kent, considers the Blackbird, Thrush, Greenfinch, and Linnet have been reduced by 50 per cent.

I have not thought it necessary to go into meteorological figures, because I am of the opinion that it was not so much the severity of the weather but the prolongation of the winter which proved so fatal. I also think that most birds met their death by starvation judging from the condition of those I examined, and large numbers, owing to their weak condition, must have fallen an easy prey to vermin.

Nature has accomplished with a single stroke the killing of many thousands of our valuable, interesting, and rare species, and it will take many years to repair that loss. Human agency could never have accomplished in the time such almost irreparable destruction.

We often read in ornithological works that such and such a species has been exterminated by collectors, but I hope in future those arm-chair naturalists who are mainly responsible for these absurd accusations, will remember that birds have many natural enemies, one of which has been the severe winter of 1916–17.

My special thanks are due to Mr G.C. Lambert for a carefully drawn-up report, also to Messrs. C.F. Stedman, Reginald Ware, H.R. Tutt, and others, not forgetting my friends in the fruit-growing industry who are keen observers.

A severe gale

From the report on the Club's meeting on 8 December 1920.

Col. Meinertzhagen made the following remarks descriptive of a recent gale in the Outer Hebrides, and its effect on bird-life:

I was in South Uist on November 15th of this year when we experienced a gale of over 90 miles an hour. Such a wind prevents one standing upright to shoot and made walking against it extremely difficult. We were at times literally carried off our feet, and for safety's sake carried our guns unloaded.

During the morning I visited the extensive grass area, called 'machar', and numerous small lochs near the sea. Whooper and Bewick Swan were common and sitting about on land in small parties. If they attempted to rise they were blown away and capsized, only to be rolled along the ground like a huge ball. Golden Plover were blown like chaff before the wind. Ringed Plover, Sanderling, Purple Sandpiper had all come inland, and when compelled to rise were carried downwind like crumpled bits of paper, capsizing whenever they attempted to land again. Mallard could rise, but could not face the wind, and were compelled to go with it. Wigeon and Golden-eye suffered the same fate. Eider-duck came in from the sea, where they could not have lived for an instant, and were sitting about on the land and on small puddles. The cock Eider was the only bird I saw which could face the wind. I saw it on two occasions, and it was a very fine example of strength and determination. Birds made about a mile an hour ground-speed, but were at frequent intervals making a minus ground-speed though still facing the wind. Hen Eider failed to face the wind, though I saw many attempt to do so.

Of smaller birds, Twites were in flocks cowering under walls; if disturbed they were dashed to the ground and were in some cases killed against walls and rocks. Blackbirds were in the same predicament. Redwing could rise from the ground, but had to turn with the wind and be blown away out of control.

Life on water for birds was impossible. Gulls were sitting on land with head held low. All Duck were on land or in very small shallow puddles. Geese were in huddled flocks sitting without sentries behind small knolls and hillocks.

The watering of young sandgrouse

E.G.B. Meade-Waldo's successes as an aviculturist were as remarkable as his achievements as a conservationist (pp. 155–63); he was clearly a man of extraordinary energy, as well as ample resources. His aviary observations on sandgrouse, summarised by him here, were later confirmed in the field by Stephen Marchant, whose original reports appeared in the *Bulletin*; the second of them (vol. 82 (1962): 123–4) is reprinted here. Since then, the whole thing has been beautifully filmed in the wild, and has been seen by millions on television.

From the report on the Club's meeting on 11 January 1922.

Sandgrouse

In reply to a question asked by Col. Meinertzhagen on behalf of Mr P.A.

Buxton on December 14th, 1921, as to whether there was any direct evidence to show that water is carried to the young in the feathers, or whether it is a myth, Mr Meade-Waldo made the following statement:

This habit was first described by me in *The Zoologist* of 1896, p. 299, and has been more fully described in *The Field* and in various papers in the *Avicultural Magazine*; but, for the benefit of any who may not have read it, I looked through my notes and find that between the years 1895 and 1915 61 broods of Sandgrouse were hatched in our aviaries. Almost all the eggs laid were fertile and hatched, and about two-thirds of the young were reared. The Sandgrouse were of three species – *Pterocles alchatus, P. exustus,* and *P. arenarius.* The great majority were of the first species, only seven broods of *P. exustus* and three broods of *P. arenarius* being reared. The breeding habits of all three species were precisely similar. The female sitting by day and the male by night, incubation lasted about 23 days, but was influenced by the weather – in very hot weather *P. exustus* hatching in 17 days on one occasion. The young are carefully attended by both parents, but are strong and feed themselves from the first. Water is conveyed to the young in the following curious manner, by the male only.

I will quote from my letter to *The Zoologist.* 'The male rubs his breast violently up and down on the ground – a motion quite distinct from dusting – and when his feathers are awry gets into his drinking-water and saturates the feathers of his underparts. When soaked he goes through the motions of flying away, nodding his head, etc.; then, remembering his family is close by, he would run to the hen, make a demonstration, when the young run out, get under him, and suck the water from his breast' – the appearance being that of a mammal suckling her young. The young pass the feathers through their bills, and keep changing places until the supply becomes exhausted.

Until the young can fly *they take water in no other way,* and the cock gives it to the young *only.*

Watering of young in *Pterocles alchata*

by S. Marchant

In a recent notice (*Bull. BOC,* vol. 81, pp. 134–41. 1961) I described aspects of breeding in the sandgrouse *Pterocles alchata* and *P. senegallus* and in particular gave an account of what was presumed to be the watering of the young by the male parent in *P. senegallus.* During 1961 further opportunities were taken of observing these birds on their breeding grounds, about 20 km nearer Baghdad than the area in which the observations were made in 1960.

On three occasions behaviour very similar to that already described for *P. senegallus* was seen with *P. alchata*. Briefly, this was as follows:

21st July. 0615 hrs. Discovered a pair with two young which were later estimated to be about ten days old. Watched till 0720 when both adults flew away and young squatted. At 0806 female returned: young got up and joined her without any abnormal behaviour. At 0813–14 male returned and settled 5 m from young: as he did so, female flew away a short distance and young immediately ran to male. For about two minutes they remained with him, evidently thrusting their heads into his belly and flank feathers, which he seemed to spread and fluff out, though my view was partly obscured by thin, low vegetation. At 0816 both young walked away from male and joined female. I immediately drove up from 150 m where I had been watching, but as I got out of the car, the young flew off down wind for 50 to 100 m. When I caught one, it had no signs of dampness on its head. Perhaps it was not likely that there would be, even though only one to two minutes at most could have elapsed between the time that the young left the male and I had caught one of them.

28th July. 0700 hrs. Discovered three adults (1 male, 2 females) with three young which were about three-quarters grown and well able to fly. It was not clear which adults owned the young and matters were further confused by other single adults coming and going, but by 0720 one female was left with the young and she left at 0722, leaving the young together and motionless. At 0731 two males landed near the young and all three at once ran up to one male. He stood erect and the young nestled around and below him, with heads inwards, like a litter of suckling puppies. At one moment I could clearly see, from about 150 m, one young with its head against the male's legs and thighs. They separated at 0734, and wandered about feeding till the female joined them at 0805.

4th August. 0615 hrs. Picked up a pair with three well-grown young of the same size as those watched on 28th July. Followed across desert for 1,500 metres till they joined a large flock of mixed adults and juveniles. The flock flew away at 0757 leaving the family behind, with a few other scattered individuals. The female parent disappeared unseen about this time. At 0804 the young squatted and the accompanying female ran on and also disappeared. At 0824 a pair flew close over the young, calling loudly. The young immediately rose and then settled with the adult pair 50 m further away on a bare desert road, when two of them at once ran up and nestled under the male, the third waiting alone indifferently for a few moments and then joining in. This 'litter of puppies' behaviour lasted for about one minute and then was broken up, all the birds walking off across the desert and feeding.

These observations seem to confirm beyond doubt the method by which these sandgrouse bring water to their young. I may add, however, that on 18th August, from 0800 to 1135 I watched a pair of *P. senegallus* with two young, no more than a week old and unable to fly. While I watched, the adults never left the young which surprised me because I had expected to see 'watering' behaviour during this period. Presumably, then, if 'watering' is performed daily, its time is more irregular than one would have imagined.

Nesting of the Fork-tailed Palm-swift

This is apparently the first published account of the nesting of either of the two South American palm-swifts. The nesting of the other species, the Pygmy Swift *Micropanyptila furcata*, is still unknown, and not much more is yet known of the breeding of the Fork-tailed Palm-swift. (The provisional identification of the Trinidad bird as *M. furcata* was incorrect; it was the Fork-tailed Palm-swift *Reinarda squamata*.)

From the report on the Club's meeting on 9 December 1931.

Mr W.L. Sclater exhibited, on behalf of Sir Charles Belcher, the nest and the skins of two young birds of a Palm-swift from Trinidad. This Swift has been provisionally identified with *Micropanyptila furcata*, recently described by Mr G.M. Sutton from Guachi, Zulia, Venezuela, in *The Auk* (1928, p. 135); this genus differs from *Reinarda*, to which the Trinidad bird was first assigned, by the absence of the feathers on the toes. However, it will not be possible to make a satisfactory identification until adult individuals can be examined. These Sir Charles Belcher has promised to endeavour to secure. At any rate, neither *Micropanyptila* or *Reinarda* have hitherto been obtained on the island of Trinidad.

The nests are placed at the base of the dead fronds on a palm-tree, probably *Mauritia flexuosa*.

The following is Sir Charles's account of the matter in his letter of September 9, 1931, to me:

> These Swifts occur, as far as I know, only in two places, and the total number so far seen cannot exceed fifteen pairs. I kept them under observation, and in July I saw one fly up into a bunch of dead palm-leaves, which satisfied me they were not Panyptilas [which attach long tubular nests to the underside of tree limbs], but I was not able to climb up to see if there were any nest. Last Sunday week, August 30, I revisited the spot, and again saw a bird fly up into the same bunch of leaves. I tapped the trunk, and *three* birds flew out, two obviously being young. I could see no nest owing to the shadows, but a curious thing happened, for, after waiting ten minutes, hoping the birds might perhaps return (which they did not do), the nest fell down!

Last Sunday I went there again, with Mr G.D. Smooker, and he and I thoroughly satisfied ourselves that the birds, of which about ten pairs were in the air, were not of any species on the Trinidad list. Yesterday we took out an expert climber, an Indian in Mr Smooker's service, and he found four nests: (a) the remains of the one that fell down, (b) an old one, (c) one building, (d) one containing two fully grown young, capable of flight, which I killed and skinned, and these skins are the ones sent herewith.

There was only one nest in each tree, and you will see from the nest, which may reach you a little later than the skins, that it is built right up at the base of the frond which is uppermost when the frond hangs down dead. What seems to happen is that the trees reach a certain height, perhaps forty feet, and then the lower leaves die, and as they die they fall at right angles to the stalk without becoming detached, and no doubt stay like that for years, for it takes a good deal of cutting with a machete to sever the frond.

The nest lowest down was about fifteen or twenty feet from the ground. The nest is a mass of multi-coloured feathers, those of Parrots and Doves being conspicuous.

Apart from the fact that this Palm-swift is new to Trinidad, nothing, so far as I have been able to ascertain, has hitherto been recorded in regard to the nesting or other habits of these birds in any of the literature I have been able to consult, so that Sir Charles's exhibit and communication is of considerable interest and novelty.

Daily altitudinal movement of the White-collared Pigeon *Columba albitorques* in the High Simien, Ethiopia

by Jeffery Boswall and Montagu Demment

At the suggestion of Derek Goodwin we have prepared this note [vol. 90 (1970): 105–7] on a daily altitudinal movement of White-collared Pigeons *Columba albitorques*. It is one of the endemic highland species of Ethiopia and is found, according to Praed and Grant (1952), in 'Eritrea to central Abyssinia'. The High Simien is the loftiest mountain range in Ethiopia and includes the highest mountain in the Empire, Ras Dejen, 15,158 feet. The range is bounded on three sides by an escarpment that rises 5,000-odd feet from the lowlands below.

One of us, J.B., visited the Simien mountains in March and April 1965 and again from 16th October to 5th November 1969. M.D. was resident on the Geech plateau for most of the period August 1968 to November 1969.

This short paper summarises the impressions of both of us.

The large majority of the observations were made from the Geech plateau. By day the birds are seen regularly on this plateau, which averages well over 12,000 feet, and also about the cliffs. In the afternoon some, if not all, the birds go down to the lowlands. Their headlong descent at high speed is a most spectacular piece of flying. In fact, to the uninitiated person, it can be quite frightening as the birds whizz past him, the wind whistling through their primaries. They usually fly within 20 feet of the slope and, on reaching a sheer precipice, drop and actually *fly* downwards at a speed that can hardly be less than 75 mph, and could be more. The reason for the high speed could be to reduce the possibility of attacks by falcons.

On the afternoon of 30th October 1969 we kept watch from a point part way down the escarpment, at about 10,900 feet, just below a buttress called Sederek, and counted the birds. They thus hurtled down the slope towards us, wings held back, and dipped over the cliff edge out of sight, doubtless dropping most of the way to the lowlands below, though it was not possible to actually observe this due to the nature of the terrain. On 17th November M.D. watched from the top of the escarpment 2 kms south-east of Sederek. The daily altitudinal range would thus be from about 12,000 feet to about 7,000 feet. The number of birds totalled for the two days, totalled for each half-hour from 14.00–14.30, to 17.30–18.00 hours were: 3, 9, 10, 16, 72, 56, 55 and 5. The frequency of party size, also totalled for the two days, was: singles, 36; two, 20; three, 7; four, 6; five, 1; six, 4; seven, 1; eight, 2; nine, 3; ten, 1; eleven, 2.

In the morning flocks of up to 50 birds, but usually of about 25, spiral their way slowly up, usually at about 8 or 9 a.m. Sometimes they rest on the cliff edge before moving 'inland' on to the plateau to feed. As might be expected, maximum numbers were seen at the lowest point of the escarpment, at the head of the Jinbar Valley, about 11,800 feet, between Emiet Gogo and Amba Ras.

During the day many birds are seen feeding in the barley fields around Geech village. Guichard (1960) says that in the Addis Ababa region the species is common on the high plateau, sometimes flocking in hundreds and doing considerable damage to newly sown wheat in June. Cultivation in Simien can be seen as high as 12,500 feet on the western side of Ras Dejen and 13,800 feet on the eastern side. We saw White-collared Pigeons up to 14,500 feet.

Night-time temperatures on the Geech plateau average 0° centigrade: day-time temperatures about 22° centigrade (based on a year's data by M.D.).

Birds are regularly seen about the highest pats of the cliffs where one gets the impression that at least some may nest. On 28th October, during a three-hour watch, J.B. saw many chases, doubtless of a sexual nature, and several display flights. In these last the bird gives a few noisy flaps of the wings, followed by a brief level glide with the wings stiffly raised at a shallow angle. The cooing rhythm is usually 'Ooh, ooooh' or sometimes 'Ooh, ooh, ooh, ooooh*ooh*'. Pitwell and Goodwin (1964) do not mention the song but the descriptions by Pitwell and Taibel in Goodwin (1967) agree with ours for the advertising coo.

Only two published references to this behaviour are known to us. Robert Cheesman (Cheesman and Sclater 1935) says:

> These pigeons roost in the cliffs of the Big Abbai (Blue Nile) canyon and those tributaries with steep-sided chasms that cut into the high plateau. They come to feed on the corn lands of the high plateau at about 8,000 feet, and in the evening return in flocks from 50 to 100, and on reaching the edge of the ravine hurl themselves over, dropping several hundreds of feet in an instant of time. They are always fast flyers.

Brown (1965 p. 56) also observed the movement in Simien:

> When spying in the evening a thousand feet or so below the top of the cliff one would be conscious of a sound of rockets rushing past. These were the pigeons shooting down from the top of the escarpment to some chosen roosting cave, perhaps 2,000 feet below. They rushed down the crag in the evening in ones and twos, but at about nine in the morning would be seen laboriously climbing up to the top again.

We feel sure that 2,000 feet is an underestimate.

Derek Goodwin tells us that converse daily movements – roosting high, feeding low – have been recorded for *Columba leuconota* in eastern Tibet, *C. arquatrix* in Africa and *Lopholaimus antarcticus* in Australia. Of these the Snow Pigeons of Asia were similar to our White-collared Pigeons in that they were feeding on cultivated land (grain stubbles).

References

Brown, L.H. (1965). *Ethiopian Episode*, Country Life, London.

Cheesman, R.E. and Sclater, W.L. (1935). On a collection of birds from North-western Abyssinia. Part II, *Ibis*, XIII: 5: 297–329.

Goodwin, D. (1967). *Pigeons and Doves of the World*, British Museum (Natural History).

Guichard, K.M. (1950). A Summary of the Birds of the Addis Ababa Region, Ethiopia. *J.E. African Nat. Hist. Soc.*, 19(5): 154–81.

Mackworth Praed, C.W. and Grant, C.H.B. (1952). *Birds of Eastern and North Eastern Africa*, vol. 1, Longmans, London.

Pitwell, L.R. and Goodwin, D. (1964). Some observations on pigeons in Addis Ababa. *Bull. Br. Orn. Cl.*, 84: 41–5.

The Cuckoo controversy

As Ian Wyllie writes in his monograph (*The Cuckoo*, 1981), 'the method by which the egg of a parasitic cuckoo is introduced into the host nest has long aroused controversy and speculation' – and nowhere more so than in the meetings of the BOC and the pages of its *Bulletin* in the 1910s and 1920s. He summarises the facts as follows:

With an egg in the oviduct ready for laying, the female Cuckoo glides like a hawk to the nest-site, landing either directly on the nest or in the vegetation nearby. As a rule, she will not know the nest's exact position within a few square metres, and probably finds it by searching the area. On reaching the nest she clings to the rim with her zygodactyl feet and balances with outstretched wings and tail. The feet remain at the back of the nest and do not enter the cup where they might damage the eggs. Invariably one of the host's eggs is picked up in the bill and held while the Cuckoo raises her abdomen over the rim of the nest to bring her cloaca over the clutch. The egg is then extruded with a shudder. The Cuckoo flies off immediately without looking at her egg, and still carrying the robbed host's egg which is swallowed whole or crushed and eaten. Occasionally one or more eggs are eaten in quick succession while the Cuckoo is at the nest, but always before she has laid her own ...

The time taken to lay the egg is remarkably swift. From the moment the Cuckoo arrives at the nest until she leaves with one of the host's eggs having laid her own, can take as little as three or four seconds. Edgar Chance found the average laying time to be less than ten seconds in Meadow Pipit nests, and Molnar (1944) recorded a duration of eight seconds in nests of Great Reed Warblers.

It should be added that, in the case of covered or otherwise rather inaccessible nests, all the evidence suggests that the Cuckoo's unusually extrusible cloaca enables her to 'squirt' the egg into the nest chamber, and its unusually thick shell prevents it from breaking.

The following extracts present some of the alternative views held on the basis of inadequate or insufficiently critical observation of what is admittedly a difficult thing to see, not least because of the speed with which it happens. The blithe acceptance of a clearly erroneous third-hand report is especially striking:

Mr Jourdain [at the Club's meeting on 9 June 1915] also read a letter from Mr H.M. Upcher to Mr Witherby, in which he stated that a friend had twice seen a Cuckoo lay its egg on the grass and place it in a Wagtail's nest by means of its bill. It was generally agreed that this method is frequently adopted by the Cuckoo, and that in the case of such species as the Willow-wren, Wren, Goldcrest, Tit-mice, etc., no other process would be possible.

A much more detailed, but equally erroneous conclusion was reached by Stuart Baker at the Club's meeting on 8 March 1922:

There is no doubt that in the vast majority of cases the egg is laid by the Cuckoo elsewhere, and deposited by means of the bill in the foster-parents' nest. I exhibit paintings of nests of some species of birds in which Cuckoos' eggs are deposited. Now, it is obvious that the Cuckoo (*C. canorus*) could not *sit* in these nests, and that the only way in which they could possibly be placed therein would be by the bill. But it is not necessary to go to India for examples of nests of this nature, for frequently the nests of Wrens, and occasionally nests of Chiff-chaffs, Willow-wrens, and other birds have had Cuckoos' eggs deposited in them without any damage having been done either to their external structure or to their small entrances. Col. Rattray, in the Murree Hills, took Cuckoos' eggs placed in nests of *Phylloscopus occipitalis* in amongst the roots of a fallen tree, in which it was only by a struggle and the loss of many neck-feathers that the Cuckoo succeeded in getting even her head to the nest. I have twice taken eggs from the nests of *Abrornis* in which not only was it impossible for the Cuckoo to insert more than her head, but from which the young Cuckoo, when hatched, could never have made an exit. Captain Bates and Mr Livesay in Kashmir took an egg of *Cuculus poliocephalus* from the nest of a Warbler built in a deserted Pigmy Woodpecker's hole. In this the Cuckoo could not even insert her head, but had dropped her own egg down the slope inside, cracking one of the eggs of the Warbler in so doing.

The general impression received from Mr Chance's beautiful film of our English Cuckoo seems to be that this particular Cuckoo laid her eggs directly into the Pipit's nest. Further careful consideration of these pictures and of Mr Chance's recorded observations make me think this impression is erroneous. In the first place, the Cuckoo is never more than a few seconds on the nest and, from what we know of other birds, oviposition takes much longer than this; again, on one occasion the Cuckoo was frightened away for half an hour, after which she returned and deposited her egg in the Pipit's nest. Now I cannot understand en egg being retained for half an hour *after* it was due to be laid. Fright might accelerate the laying of an egg, and all of us must have seen many instances of this; but I know of no instance of retarded production under such circumstances. Again, Mr Chance's pictures show that though his Cuckoos seem to get their breasts and foreparts well *into* the nest, the other end is right up against, or actually projects over, the edge of the nest, and I doubt if an egg so laid would not fall out rather than into the nest. I was much puzzled over this until I watched the photo of the first Cuckoo, which comes down and stands a few seconds outside the nest. This bird obviously has something in her gullet sufficient to distend it and make the feathers all stick out. This something is in all probability her own egg. When she comes out the other bird's egg is visible in the bill, and her throat is relaxed and the feathers lie flat. Again, we should consider what are the Cuckoo's motions in the nest, so far as can be judged by the films. She gets into the nest as speedily as possible, and at once bends down her head under her body. My own idea is that she now regurgitates and deposits her own egg in the nest, takes up one of the foster-parent's eggs in her bill, and flies off.

Mr Charles Inglis and I myself have both been fortunate enough to see *Clamator jacobinus* place her own egg in the nest of *Turdoides terricolor*. In neither case did the bird get into the nest, but leant right over it, and when she flew off in each case the egg of the fosterer was visible in the Cuckoo's bill, though in neither case could we detect any sign of the egg in the Cuckoo's bill when she came up. In the case in which I saw the operation performed, the Cuckoo dropped down on the grass just a few yards in front of me and with her back towards me, put her head right down, heaved, and then flew up to the Babbler's nest, whence she took an egg and returned to the ground, and again back at once to the nest, having apparently exchanged the Babbler's for her own egg, for when I went up to the nest, there was the Cuckoo's egg on the top of three of the Babbler's and the fourth was lying on the ground broken – smashed, I think, by the bird, startled by suddenly catching sight of me. This idea of regurgitating the egg struck me when I saw the part of Mr Chance's film showing the parents feeding their young. In this the male regurgitates twice and brings up insects which he passes over to the female, yet the swelling in the gullet is not noticeable, but the head and shoulder action of the male is exactly like that of the female Cuckoo on the nest. To this question, as to how the female Cuckoo deposits her egg in another bird's nest, I would, therefore, venture to suggest that she does so with her bill, carrying the egg in her gullet until such time as she thinks appropriate for the job, when she flies down to the nest, regurgitates, drops the egg in, and flies off, generally taking one of the fosterer's in exchange.

P.F. Bunyard, a well-known oologist but obviously far from open-minded as far as the Cuckoo question was concerned, contributed to the controversy at the Club's meeting on 12 October 1927:

Mr Bunyard gave a very interesting account of his experiences in watching, at Cliffe-at-Hoo, Kent, the same Cuckoo which he had under observation in 1925 and 1926:

On June 1st he watched the Cuckoo go to a Reed-warbler's nest, cling on to the sides, and go through the same performance as described in the *Bulletin* for last October (cf. xlvii, p. 45, 1926). This time, however, when she withdrew her head for the second time, Mr Bunyard observed that she had a Reed-warbler's egg in her beak, which she swallowed whole and 'then thrust her head into the nest for the third time, as though she were trying to secure the remaining Warbler's egg, threw herself back to the left, and took off.'

Leaving his 'hide' Mr Bunyard went and examined the nest, but was disappointed to find only one Reed-warbler's egg – there were originally two – and no Cuckoo's. As there had been no attempt at a deposition, the whole proceedings had only been a raid.

On June 28th Mr Bunyard paid a final visit to Cliffe, when he again had an unobstructed view of the Reed-warbler's nest with two eggs. After watching from a 'hide' eight feet from the nest for about an hour, he had a clear view of the Cuckoo on a thorn-bush, and it certainly had no egg in its beak. She disappeared, and then a few minutes later he saw her approaching the nest, again no egg in the beak!, on reaching which 'she clung on to the side, as previously seen on two occasions, with her back towards the 'hide', but slightly sideways with her shoulders level with the top of the nest. She then thrust her head and neck into the nest, slightly withdrew, repeating the operation, and on withdrawing I saw she had a Warbler's egg in her bill. She then turned towards the 'hide', took off gracefully, and flew away.' Mr Bunyard immediately examined the nest, which now contained one Warbler's egg and one Cuckoo's egg, the whole operation taking only eight seconds.

When at the nest, Mr Bunyard said the Cuckoo's 'body and limp drooping wings almost concealed the nest from my view. She neither went on to, or over, the nest, and obviously the only possible way her egg could have reached its destination was by regurgitation.'

Mr Bunyard went on to say that during his many visits to Cliffe he 'saw absolutely nothing to support the theory of normal oviposition, which has no scientific data to support it, is economically unsound, and physically impossible.'

The theory of regurgitation, he pointed out, appears first to have been put forward by A.H. Meiklejohn in the *Zoologist* for 1900, but Le Vaillant seems to have been the first discoverer that the White-bellied Didric Cuckoo (*Lampromorpha caprius* Bodd.) of South Africa carried her egg in the throat.

Fabre (*Animal Life in Field and Garden*, p. 60), Mr Bunyard further remarked, definitely states, but on what authority he did not know, that the Cuckoo lays its egg on the ground, swallows it, and regurgitates it into the nest of the fosterer.

Bunyard was answered at a subsequent meeting by D.W. Musselwhite:

At the October meeting of the Club Mr P.F. Bunyard described the actions of a Cuckoo at Cliffe-at-Hoo, which convinced him that the bird deposited its egg in a Reed-warbler's nest after regurgitation. Many, including myself, did not think his evidence was nearly strong enough, and I said so at the time. Today I am even more convinced that Mr Bunyard has not proved his case, and I think it only right I should give you my reasons.

First of all, let me say that Mr G.J. Scholey, who was present at the meeting in October, and Mr Bunyard have been co-operating in this work at Cliffe-at-Hoo, and together have had this individual Cuckoo under observation for the past three seasons, 1925/6/7. At the above meeting Mr Bunyard exhibited a series of forty-seven eggs laid by this bird, including sixteen laid in 1925, which made it obvious that the bird watched in 1925 was the same as that observed in 1927.

Mr Bunyard in the *Bulletin*, p. 32, states that he 'saw absolutely nothing to support the theory of normal oviposition, which has no scientific data to support it, is economically unsound, and physically impossible.' I regard this as a most remarkable statement, and it is all the more so since Mr Scholey in watching the same bird has evidently seen it many times lay its eggs in the usual way in the nests of Reed-warblers.

In the *Country Side* for July 1925 Mr Scholey writes as follows:

> The present season just concluded found another reed-warbler cuckoo upon the same territory. She laid sixteen eggs on alternate days from May 31st to June 30th inclusive. Unlike her predecessor this bird, instead of dropping into marsh grass for half an hour or so prior to depositing, would fly to the tall hawthorn nearest the nest about to be used, where she would sit sometimes right over the nest for a corresponding period exactly as her predecessor did in the grass. She would fly direct to the nest from the hawthorn, which, of course, she had located some days beforehand, deposit her egg and be away in from five to ten seconds. Further, the reed-warblers' nests used by this bird were never tilted sideways, and observations at close quarters (eight feet) *proved beyond doubt that she sat upon these nests and laid her egg in a normal manner.* Now, had this bird deposited otherwise, when did she lay her egg and pick it up when I had her under observation for half an hour previously?

Mr Bunyard seems to have overlooked this note, since at the end of his report he says 'that he would like to support the various statements made by Mr G.J. Scholey from time to time in the Press and which he had ample opportunity of verifying.' I think, therefore, that some explanation is necessary, as evidently Mr Bunyard's observations in 1927 do not coincide with those made by Mr Scholey on the same Cuckoo two years earlier.

With regard to this Cuckoo's actions when it was alleged to have regurgitated its egg, Mr Bunyard has admitted that the bird had its back to him and the wings were limp and drooping.

As the body and partly spread wings of a Cuckoo would span about three

Reed-warblers' nests, I think it will at once be seen how speculative a definite statement would be as to how the egg was deposited, especially as the whole procedure did not occupy more than eight seconds. There is no doubt that, as the bird had its back to the hide, the observer was at a great disadvantage.

The controversy continued, until to all intents and purposes it was settled by Edgar Chance (*The Truth about the Cuckoo*, 1940). Discussions often became heated, and finally, as described by W.H. Thorpe in his reminiscences of the Club (vol. 100: 34–5), resulted in a strangely ambivalent statement by the Committee:

There were, however, one or two members whose activities generally ensured that meetings were enlivened by the squibs and firecrackers of controversy. The standard topics for argument were usually provided by the oologists, and particularly those who were interested in the breeding habits of the Cuckoo. P.F. Bunyard, a great egg collector, and E.P. Chance, were usually present and one felt rather disappointed if they didn't start to erupt. Once they did so there were plenty of others ready, indeed eager, to join the show. One could be fairly sure that the Rev. F.C.R. Jourdain, a vigorous controversialist, E.C. Stuart Baker and perhaps H.F. Witherby would show a sudden rise in temperature. In 1924 the situation became so explosive that the Committee published the following paragraphs amongst others:

> The Committee ... desires to make it clear ... that ... their appointment of a Committee to obtain, if possible, direct evidence of the method of deposition of the egg by the Cuckoo must not be taken to imply that they subscribed to Mr Chance's remarks or that they had any intention of discrediting Mr Bunyard's account of what he had observed. Their sole desire was to assist in obtaining direct evidence of the method of deposition, by the examination, if possible, of a Cuckoo about to lay.

Even the showing of a film by Mr Oliver G. Pike depicting a cuckoo actually depositing en egg in a Meadow Pipit's nest by no means stilled the controversy!

What became of this Cuckoo Committee? Nothing appears in subsequent issues of the *Bulletin*; perhaps they realised that their remit was an impossible one for a committee, and tacitly left it to time to provide the answer.

Taxonomy, systematics and evolution

A large part of the *Bulletin* has been devoted to descriptive taxonomy and systematics, especially at the level of the species and subspecies. Far more new forms have been described in its pages than in any other journal. For the first forty years or so of the *Bulletin*'s life, however, understanding of the processes of evolution had hardly progressed beyond the stage reached by Darwin; the science of genetics was in its infancy. Hence the few theoretical contributions and discussions of topics such as geographical variation and adaptation are no longer very relevant or, indeed, even historically of much interest. Thus in 1915 Lord Rothschild opened a discussion on the effect of environment on the evolution of species with the following general statement:

> It is much less easy, at the present day, to discuss Environment and its influence on Evolution than it was a few years ago, owing to the experiments carried out in connection with the study of the 'Mendelian Law'. This study and the experiments connected with it have led many biologists to the conviction that all variation is fortuitous, and that the fixity of certain types and the continuance of evolution are entirely due to the action of the Mendelian Law. It would take much longer than the time at my disposal to discuss adequately these experiments, or to explain why the exponents of 'Mendelism' have, in many instances, come to the conclusions which they expound. In this discussion I propose to follow the lines of reasoning which have led to my personal conclusions, and to leave it to others to prove or disprove these conclusions as well as they are able. It is my opinion that climatic and other local conditions start the variation, and that the Darwinian law of the survival of the fittest directs and maintains this variation, but that the Mendelian law, by hastening the process of evolution in the direction in which it began, finally completes the process.

Of more modern relevance are the discussions of subspecies. Stuart Baker's address, given in 1920, starts off well with a useful and valid definition of a subspecies, but soon becomes bogged down in what now seems a rather sterile discussion of the 'germ-plasm' (a vague term, more or less corresponding to what would now be called the gene-complex or genome) and how it interacts with the environment. Having dealt with that, he returns to a useful discussion, based largely on personal experience, containing much that is relevant today. Hartert's briefer contribution, which followed, corrects Stuart Baker on one important point; while Jourdain's remarks add little of substance but throw light on reactions in this country when subspecies were coming into general use. With David Lack's contribution in 1946 we enter a different era; it is as cogent a statement as one could find of the value of the subspecies concept and the difficulties of expressing it in trionomial nomenclature. It is also an early example of the use of Huxley's symbol for the cline, which has obvious advantages but has not been generally adopted. The subject is further discussed by Clancey, who advocated the naming of all finely differentiated forms and was convincingly opposed by Southern, while Tucker added a characteristically clear and well-balanced opinion.

The question of nomenclature – the rules governing the use of scientific names, in itself without any biological content – has never been a prominent feature of the *Bulletin*. It was, however, amusingly dealt with by W.S. Flower in his Chairman's address in 1930, which opened as follows:

> Nomenclature, 'which owing to its contentious nature I have studied to avoid' wrote Alfred Newton in 1896, is a subject from which there is no escape. At first sight it may appear nothing but a trying and tiresome *incubus* that has descended on innocent ornithologists in their sleep, but when fairly tackled it proves to be a subject in itself not only of interest, but also, now and again, of amusement.

A minor controversy in nomenclature in which Captain Grant was opposed to Dean Amadon is resuscitated on p. 115. The new resolutions recently put forward by the International Commission for Zoological Nomenclature, if adopted, will mark the end of such controversies, one would hope, for all time.

E.C. Stuart Baker on 'The value of subspecies to the field naturalist' (11 February 1920)

I must first apologise to my audience tonight for the fact that practically all I am about to say has already appeared in the *Journal of the Bombay Natural History Society*, though I then wrote purely from the point of view of the Indian field naturalist.

Perhaps, as a preliminary to our discussion, I should state what is my idea of a subspecies. It is as follows:

A subspecies is a geographical race or variation, differing in some respect from the form first described as a species, yet linked with it by other intermediate forms found in inter-vening areas. It is essential, however, that the variation before it is named shall be proved to be stable within a certain definite area.

From my definition it will be seen that I consider a subspecies to be merely a species in the making, and that subspecies become full species when Nature, in the course of evolution, has eliminated the intervening forms. Some natu-ralists hold that this theory is wrong, and say that in a species the germ-plasm is different in itself and in its potentialities, and that, therefore, subspecies can never become species. I quite agree that in every true species the germ-plasm differs from that of every other species, but the fact that it is so is only because it has arrived at a stage of evolution parallel with the evolu-tion in its colour, structural, or other superficial variation from which we decide its rank as a species or subspecies.

The point to be remembered is that evolution in the germ-plasm proceeds *pari passu* with external evolution, though it is not until it has reached an advanced stage that it permanently contains the inherent potentialities which pass on from one generation to another the external features caused by envi-ronment.

Thus a species transferred from its original environment may or may not gradually evolve external variations due to its new surroundings, but the changes, if any, will be assumed by degrees, and as they become fixed, the germ-plasm also, gradually and equally influenced, arrives at a stage when it is capable of passing on these variations in a stable form, until once more there are further geographical or climatic changes. At the same time, the influences brought to bear on other individuals of the same species less far removed from their original habitat will be less pronounced, and we thus get the half-way individuals which link the two extreme forms together, until, as I have already said, these die out and leave the two extremes constantly and definitely cut off from one another.

All birds come from ancestors comparatively few in number, who in turn work back to a still smaller number of reptile-like forms, and thence back and back to still more primitive forms, multicellular and unicellular proto-plasms, etc., and no one can contend that the evolution of the protoplasm has remained quiescent all this time.

Classification of the living members of the Class 'Aves', like every other classification, is intended to simplify, or make easy, the attainment of know-ledge. In the present instance, the division of species should assist in the acquirement of knowledge, both of ornithology as a whole, as well as of each individual species, its life history, and all other facts connected with it. If the classification employed helps towards this end, it is scientific; if, on the other hand, it renders the acquisition of knowledge more difficult, it is not scien-tific, and should be discarded.

When ornithology was in its infancy, birds were lumped together under one name in the most extraordinary way, and at this period much the same degree of nomenclature obtained amongst civilised people as obtains today among savage tribes. Thus there were groups of birds known as Vultures, Eagles, Ducks, Storks, Owls, Flycatchers, and so on; sometimes these were again divided into 'large' or 'small', and sometimes a second qualifying name was added, denoting some conspicuous character. As time progressed, these larger divisions were gradually broken into smaller and smaller ones, until eventually most birds which differed conspicuously from others had a definite trivial name. To this succeeded a time when Latin and Greek, or pseudo-Latin and Greek, names were given in addition to the local trivial names, thus enabling workers to recognise the bird spoken or written about, whatever the language employed in the context. At this period, and for a long time after, fresh discoveries were constantly being made; unknown countries were still plentiful, and naturalists had more than sufficient to employ them in working out new species on the very broadest lines. Under such circumstances, minor differences were either overlooked or ignored, whilst the causes for these same differences were never sought for.

Now, however, we live in a time when there are but few countries left to explore, and novelties of specific rank are few and far between, consequently minor differences attract attention to a far greater degree than was previously the case. Together with these differences, the worker now seeks to elucidate their causes, thus necessitating a knowledge of their life history, quite unnecessary so long as one was content to acknowledge only such striking features as were visible without search to everyone. A very much finer division of living objects becomes possible to the modern ornithologist, for whom the material to be worked on has already been collected and classified on broader lines by the naturalists of previous generations.

This much for subspecies, but having decided that we are to recognise these, how are we to distinguish by words one subspecies or geographical race from another? We may decide to use binomials, only adding some description which shall denote what particular race each belongs to, or we may add a description of the geographical area to which it is confined – sometimes quite a lengthy matter, – or we may adopt the quickest and simplest plan and add a third name to the binomial, and so come to the now universally adopted system of trinomialism, i.e. three names which, without further description, show to what genus and species each geographical race belongs.

But before a subspecies can be determined, two things are essential: first, that field naturalists should collect from various areas material which can be assembled in one museum, and, secondly, that the museum man, with the help of his library of reference and such other collections as may be at his disposal, should patiently work out the material supplied.

It is evident, therefore, that whereas the field naturalist may be able to do his own work and, later on, part of that of the museum man also, the museum man cannot do a stroke of work without the help of the field worker.

To the modern field naturalist one would therefore imagine trinomialism and all that it includes must be of the most absorbing interest, for it is only he who can supply us with the factors to elucidate all the causes giving rise to the variations which form geographical races. There is still much work for him to do.

At present our knowledge of cause and effect is very crude. Certain broad rules we do know, but very little of the minutiae or of the way in which these same broad rules conflict or combine.

We know that humidity generally means deep and brilliant colouring, and drought the reverse. Dense tropical forests run much to black, but often a combination with it of most vivid colours. Snow and ice require their inhabitants to seek immunity from danger in white pelts or plumage. Animals and birds in deserts require sandy or pale plumage corresponding to their environment, and so on. We already know that some changes occur far more quickly than others, as for instance Beebe's Dove, which changed from one race to another in its own lifetime, whilst, on the other hand, there are numerous instances of game and other birds, such as Sparrows in America, Mynas in Australia, in which there is as yet no apparent change taking place. In the latter we have the result of many generations of birds from which to draw our conclusions, but in Beebe's bird we do not know what the result of the individual change would have been on the next generation, and whether the protoplasm had acquired the potentialities that a permanent change would entail.

Even here, in our little home isles, it is only quite recently that our naturalists have been able to show that we have stable local varieties among our resident or breeding birds. Naturally, the range of variation is not what it is in larger countries – such as my own field of work, India. Here we find great alluvial plains and stupendous mountains, wonderful forests and parching deserts, burning heat and bitter cold, regions where the maximum rainfall of the world is registered and others where in some years no rain falls. But in Great Britain we have our comparatively dry areas and wet areas, our colder and our warmer counties, our forests and our open moors, so even here we find that geographical conditions suffice to induce certain corresponding variations in their inhabitants, and as time goes on we shall certainly be able yet to find more matter of interest, more riddles of evolution to solve, and more material for future naturalists to work on.

When zoological specimens were first collected, data were for the most part neglected, and to such an extent that there are many instances of birds being named after countries in which they have never occurred. The collectors having collected from many places made no notes, and when they returned home trusted to a memory which played them false, with the result mentioned.

Nowadays, the would-be successful field naturalist, who wishes to advance knowledge in any degree, must be a man of the closest observation, of keen intelligence, and of most careful, methodical habits. No one dare trust to memory now, and a careful record must be kept of anything and everything which may assist the museum man in collating his facts and basing his arguments to prove whatever theories he may be able to propound.

It was as a field naturalist myself that I first felt that binomialism did not suffice for my working, and arguments between myself and the late Mr E.W. Oates arose simply because he could not then accept the now admitted fact that subspecies are much more common than species, and that geographical races require determination even more than original species, and I am sure my difficulties must have been those of many other youngsters also. It was Dr Hartert in a little note on the Minivets who first put me on the right trail, and from that moment my difficulties practically disappeared, and I found in trinomialism the solution of all my difficulties.

In foreign countries, and especially in tropical areas, where most collecting is carried out in winter, it is often most perplexing when one has to deal with both breeding and migratory individuals of the same species, and here the field naturalist alone can help us out of our difficulties, and the material obtained by oologists in the way of breeding birds is of incomparable value. Take, for instance, our Little Ringed Plovers. We have breeding races in areas ranging from W. Europe to Japan, but in winter all three races are found within the Indian Empire. Again, the Kentish Plover is a similar instance. We have *alexandrinus* breeding from England to Quetta (Meinertzhagen), *dealbatus* breeding in China, etc., and *seebohmi* breeding in India and Ceylon, and all three are found in India in winter.

To the oologist also the interest of geographical races is quite as fascinating as to the purely bird man, though so far the effect of environment has been much neglected in oology, and we really know practically nothing about it, yet in many instances eggs vary geographically, even more than the birds which lay them.

I have never been able to fathom the reasons of those who inveigh against trinomialism. As a rule, it is merely the allegation that we are making it harder for the individual in question to remember names. So, too, those who curse the modern ornithologist for creating – as they call it – new names, generally found their reasons for the accusation on the inconvenience it causes them personally.

There *can* be but one correct name for a bird, and naturalists of the calibre who complain because their personal convenience and sympathies are not consulted forget that no generation works for itself alone and its own pleasure. It is the duty of each generation to put classification and nomenclature – amongst other things – on as stable a basis as possible for the generations to follow, and the only way to do this is to make some definite rule as to nomenclature and adhere to it. The rule made by the International Congress and universally agreed to is that priority of nomenclature shall be strictly adhered to with effect from the date of the tenth edition of Linnaeus (1758), the founder of binomialism. This, of course, means that from time to time some long-accepted name has to be discarded for another, hitherto over-looked and unknown, which preceded it. Naturally our own sympathies are in favour of the continuation of the name we have known all our lives, but our children will always know it by the new name and will not be bothered with this question of sympathy, if we are only consistent, and adopt, as soon as it is ascertained, the name to which the bird is properly entitled. If orni-thologists of the present generation do their duty without first stopping to consider whether it will inconvenience them personally, those of coming generations will have but little left to do in reference to classification and nomenclature. All this, the rough foundation-work of ornithology, will have been threshed out by ourselves and, perhaps, those who next succeed us. Those to come later will be employed in elucidating cause and effect, not in finding out what is, but in ascertaining *why* it is and *how* it has become so. The ornithologist will not want to find out in what respect one bird differs from another, where it lives, and how it feeds. All this will be ready prepared for him to acquire speedily from books, and it will be his duty to continue the investigations into reasons and results, and to tabulate what he learns as the basis of work for yet future generations.

So too, the oologist will no longer want to know what bird lays what kind of egg, but will be discovering why each particular kind of egg is laid, how and why it is pigmented in a thousand different ways, together with the attendant anatomical and biological circumstances.

Practically all scientific zoological research resolves itself into an endless inquiry into the ways of evolution. Each successful naturalist adds during his life something to the accumulated mass of accepted facts upon which others shall build up either additional facts, or shall make some discovery which shall further enlighten humanity upon the ways and means of the great mystery of creation and perpetuation of life by evolution.

To me it seems that when we find out a few facts entitling geographical races to trinomials, we are adding a few bricks to the foundation of the building whose coping-stone shall be complete knowledge.

Dr Ernst Hartert said he, needless to say, agreed with almost every word Mr Stuart Baker said, but he objected to make supposed intergradation between two forms a criterion of the subspecies. Though we are convinced that inter-gradation between subspecies must have existed, and exists now in many cases, there were, nevertheless, numerous instances in which no intergrad-ation could be traced – in fact, we seldom found it to exist. This was the case with many forms replacing each other on continents, but still more often, of course, with island forms. American ornithologists for a long time regarded the existence of intergradation necessary for a supposed subspecies, in consequence of which they treated island forms, which were the most typical examples of subspecies, as species; but they had now recognised the fallacy of their treatment and looked upon representative island forms as subspecies.

The question having been raised, how a subspecies should be defined, he wished to repeat what he had often said elsewhere, that he regarded as subspecies forms which agreed in their main characters while they differed in details (either of colour, markings, or dimensions), *and represented each other geographically* – or that subspecific characters were '*differences combined with geographical separation*', agreement in structure and general features, of course, being established.

With regard to different habits these need not always be peculiarities of distinct subspecies, but often were due to different conditions, such as a more inhabited and more cultivated country, where the habits easily changed. Thus it was merely the result of conditions which changed the Blackbird, Thrush, and Wood-pigeon from a shy forest bird to a town bird, and that may also partly be the reason for the different habits of the continental and the very distinct British Robin.

The Rev. F.C.R. Jourdain remarked that many members of the Union restricted their interests to British birds and were inclined to look askance at subspecies generally, with the exception of one or two cases, in which they had personal experience of two subspecies side by side, such as the case of the Pied and White Wagtails or the Yellow and Blue-headed Wagtails. These were readily and universally recognised, but for consistency's sake were elevated to the rank of separate species, as was done by the earlier writers. Although the differences between an adult male *Mot. a. lugubris* and one of *M. a. alba* were sufficiently obvious, there were, however, other subspecies which were not so readily distinguishable, so that even in the pages of the *Ibis* one found '*M. lugubris*' recorded as plentiful in Mesopotamia (*Ibis*, 1914, p. 390) by a good field naturalist, some 2,000 miles east of its normal range! Similarly, the Yellow Wagtails from the Caspian approach very closely to our British race, and it was not possible to pronounce on the validity of a subspecies without having a series of all the known forms before one. To come to a final decision on a point of this kind, when one was only acquainted with the two forms which occur locally, was only a sign of ignorance. Speaking from personal experience, the speaker had noticed that English field workers, though deeply prejudiced against the principle of recognising subspecific races, nevertheless were quick to appreciate these differences in life, and the characteristics of the Continental Robin and Stonechat were at once noted when the birds were first met with in the field.

The fact was that the study of local races could only be satisfactorily carried on in one or two of our great museums, where large series from all parts of the world were available for comparison. It was an unfortunate weakness that the work of nomenclature should be restricted to those, not necessarily field workers themselves, who profited by the actual collector's labours. As a result, we found innumerable races named after the members of museum staffs – neither descriptive nor geographically useful, and conveying nothing to the student of the future. All the honours, such as they were, fell to the describer, and it was not unnatural that in consequence we found local races described in many cases on somewhat trivial and insufficient grounds. But, apart from this blot, the impetus given to the study of ornithology was so great that its value could hardly be over-estimated, especially with regard to migration. The occurrence of a dark-breasted Barn Owl in December in England, or a grey-backed Jay in Norfolk, would have been quite meaningless to a British ornithologist 60 or 70 years ago; whether a Nutcracker had a thin or thick bill merely led to wild suggestions that these characters were sexual. To us these occurrences were fraught with meaning, and it was due to the labours of those who had studied the question that this gate of knowledge had been opened to us.

Taxonomy of the Robin *Erithacus rubecula* (Linn.)

Mr David Lack sent the following paper in amplification of his remarks and exhibits at the meeting on January 16, 1946:

The genus

The Robin or Redbreast, originally named *Motacilla rubecula* by Linnaeus, was later separated off in a genus of its own, usually *Erithacus*, created by Cuvier in 1801, but originally spelt *Erythacus*. Other generic names, such as *Dandalus* and *Rubecula*, have been used at times. The genus *Erithacus* at one time included four species, the European *rubecula* (Linn.), the Persian *hyrcanus* Blanford, the Canary Island *superbus* Koenig, and the Japanese *akahige* (Temminck). However, Hartert (1910) merged *hyrcanus* and *superbus* as subspecies of *rubecula*, and moved *akahige* to the genus *Luscinia*. With the former decision all modern workers agree, but the latter requires further discussion.

The male Japanese Robin *L. akahige* has a colour pattern more like that of *rubecula* than any other species, with a brown back, red breast and white abdomen. Its chief distinctions are the longer beak, the extension of rufous on to the upper parts, particularly the tail, and the band of grey below the red breast. In regard to the two former differences, the Persian Robin, *E. rubecula hyrcanus*, is somewhat intermediate, though decidedly closer to typical *rubecula* than to *akahige*. This might suggest that Hartert was wrong in taking *akahige* out of the genus *Erithacus*. However, *akahige* is sexually dimorphic (like the *Cyanosylvia* subsection of the genus *Luscinia*), and the plumage of the female is closely similar to that of various other species of *Luscinia*. Further, the recently recorded habits of *akahige* are quite distinct from those of *rubecula*. Jahn (1942) describes the song as a short, beautiful trill, with long pauses between. The singing shakes the whole body, and the bird has a 'song-ecstasy' with erect tail, hanging wings, and upward-pointing beak. The song and song-attitudes are quite different from those of *rubecula*. Further, the 'ticking' call typical of *rubecula* is not found, and the alarm note resembles that of a Nightingale (*Luscinia megarhynchos*). These ethological characters are more convincing than plumage in denoting the systematic position of *akahige*.

As a result of Hartert's treatment, with which thus far I agree, the genus *Erithacus* becomes monotypic. To justify the retention of a monotypic genus, the species concerned must be highly distinctive. But this is not the case in *Erithacus rubecula*, and the differences used by Hartert (1910) and Witherby (1938) to separate it from *Luscinia* are extremely slight. Further, the genus *Luscinia* includes two subsections, the Nightingales (*Luscinia* sens. strict.) and the Bluethroats (formerly separated as *Cyanosylvia*). When plumage and habits are considered, the Bluethroats seem closer to the Robin than they are to the Nightingales. If this is correct, only two alternatives are open, either to re-erect *Cyanosylvia*, or to sink *Luscinia* (created by Forster in 1817) into *Erithacus*. The latter procedure was in fact adopted by Seebohm (1881) in the British Museum Catalogue, and seems to me the better of the two. However, I am not proposing to revise the genus *Luscinia*, so leave this point to a subsequent worker. It may be added that, should *Luscinia* (including *Cyanosylvia*) be merged with *Erithacus*, there is probably a case, too, for merging other closely related genera. These would include the Rubythroat *Calliope calliope* (Pallas), Swinhoe's Robin *Larvivora sibilans* Swinhoe, and the Blue Robin *Larvivora cyane* (Pallas), all of which were already placed in *Luscinia* by Hartert (1910) (see Jahn, 1942, for habits), and perhaps the White-throated Robin *Irania gutturalis* (Guérin) and others. There would seem to have been a plethora of monotypic genera, and genera with very few species, related to *Erithacus* and *Luscinia*. Before reaching a final decision on this matter, the systematist would be advised to study the habits of the birds in question in their Asiatic homeland.

Eastern subspecies of *E. rubecula*

The Persian form *E. rubecula hyrcanus* Blanford is readily distinguishable from typical *rubecula*, being rather browner above, a much deeper red on the breast, rufous on the long upper tail-coverts, and longer in beak. Measured from nostril to tip of culmen, the beak of *hyrcanus* is about 1 mm longer than that of typical *rubecula*.

The region north-west of the breeding range of *hyrcanus* is inhabited by *E. r. caucasicus* Buturlin. This is intermediate in every respect between *hyrcanus* and typical *rubecula*, differing from *hyrcanus* in being greyer above, less deep red below, less rufous on the upper tail-coverts, and shorter in beak. Most of the near-East specimens in the British Museum (Natural History) and in Col. Meinertzhagen's collection were taken in winter quarters, and it proved impossible to divide these into two distinct groups, one of *hyrcanus* and the other of *caucasicus*, as the two intergrade, as does *caucasicus* with *rubecula*. I therefore suggest that the facts are more truly represented by suppressing the name *caucasicus*, and that the breeding population of the southern Caucasus should be written as *rubecula* ≥ *hyrcanus*. The boundaries of the region occupied by this transitional population are not yet known.

I have not seen two races named from the Soviet Union, namely *tartaricus* Grote and *ciscaucasicus* Buturlin. Grote (1928) describes *tartaricus* as lighter above and paler below than typical *rubecula* from Sweden. Its breeding range is the Ural region. The race *ciscaucasicus* is described as browner above than typical *rubecula*, but somewhat greyer and more olive than *caucasicus* (Grote, 1929). This indicates that it is part of the transitional *rubecula* ≤ *hyrcanus* population, and its breeding range on the northern side of the Caucasus supports this view.

I have not seen the form *xanthothorax* Salvadori and Festa, named from six specimens from Rhodes in February and March (see Hartert, 1922, p. 2169). It seems unlikely that these individuals were breeding on Rhodes, and the reddish tint on the upper tail-coverts strongly suggests that they were birds from the region inhabited in summer by *rubecula* ≥ *hyrcanus*.

The Atlantic islands subspecies

Passing from the eastern to the south-western end of the range of the Robin, the Canary Island form *E. r. superbus* Koenig is strikingly distinct, differing from typical *rubecula* particularly in its rich red breast and very white abdomen, while its upper parts are more olive-brown. It is also smaller, the wing averaging 3 to 4 mm shorter than in typical *rubecula*. The beak is proportionately, and actually, slightly longer than in *rubecula*. These size trends accord with Bergmann's and Allen's rules respectively. *E. r. superbus* is confined to the central Canary Islands of Gran Canaria and Tenerife.

The western Canary Islands, the Azores and Madeira are inhabited by grey-backed, pale-breasted Robins indistinguishable in plumage from typical *rubecula* from Sweden. The wing-length of the insular birds is on the average a little smaller, but the overlap is too great for subspecific separation. Formerly they were named *microrhynchus* (Reichenow), but the implied shorter beak is not a valid character. Hence these birds should be termed *rubecula*, though isolated from typical Continental *rubecula* not only by the sea, but by populations of different colour in Portugal and Britain.

It seems astonishing that the Azores, Madeira and the western Canary Islands should be inhabited by one form when the central Canary Islands, only twenty miles from the western group, are inhabited by a strikingly different form, *superbus*. The situation is even more remarkable if the birds from the western Canary Islands are of the same form as those breeding in Scandinavia, over 2,000 miles away.

British subspecies

The British Robin, *E. rubecula melophilus* Hartert, differs from typical *rubecula* in being more olive-brown, less grey, on the upper parts, and a deeper and more orange-red on the breast. Measurements are similar. Typical *rubecula* from northern, central and eastern Europe are readily separated by colour from typical *melophilus* from central England and further west. However, J.M. Harrison (1942) has shown that in eastern England, in Kent, some individuals have a breast which is almost or quite as pale as in typical *rubecula*, though the back is normally more olive. Dr. Harrison kindly lent me his large Kentish series, and I fully support his findings. Every gradation in breast-colour is found between pale *rubecula*-like and dark *melophilus*-like specimens. Dr. Harrison considers that some of these birds were probably wintering Continental *rubecula*, but others were obtained so late in April that breeding birds would seem to be involved. Further, some Suffolk Robins agree in appearance with the Kentish birds. In western Holland, too, the breeding Robins are decidedly more olive on the upper parts, and have a tendency to be more orange below, than typical *rubecula* from Germany and eastern Holland, as shown by the large series in the Leiden Museum. Kleinschmidt's race *monnardi* (see Hartert, 1922) was based on birds intermediate in appearance between *rubecula* and *melophilus*. Likewise Lebeurier and Rapine (1936) separated the birds of Basse-Bretagne as *armoricanus*, but in all respects these individuals seem intermediate between *rubecula* and *melophilus*. Again, five specimens taken by P.A. Clancey near Dornoch in Sutherland are slightly paler on the breast, and extremely slightly greyer on the upper parts, particularly the head, than typical *melophilus*.

To conclude, the boundary between typical *rubecula* and *melophilus* is not a sharp one formed by the sea, and there is a transitional population, which may be written as *rubecula* ≷ *melophilus*, breeding in the coastal regions on either side of the North Sea and English Channel. Moving from east to west through this transitional population, from Continental *rubecula* to British *melophilus*, one finds that the birds tend to assume the olive colour on the back before the breast becomes a deeper orange.

It should not, of course, be supposed that, at any one place in the transitional area, every individual is uniform in colour. At each place there are some comparatively pale and other comparatively dark breasted individuals, some comparatively grey-backed and other comparatively olive-backed specimens. Indeed, this appears to hold in all parts of the Robin's range. It is the average which gradually shifts.

North African subspecies

The Algerian robin was separated by Hartert (1910) as *witherbyi*. Further east, Bannerman named *lavaudeni* from Tunisia, but Hartert (1928) considered this form inseparable from *witherbyi*. The type-locality of *witherbyi* is in Lat. 36° 26′N and Long. 2° 28′E. The taxonomic position would have been easier if the type-locality had been further east, as the Tunisian birds represent the culmination of a trend of variation away from typical *rubecula*, which starts in central Spain and continues through southern Spain, the North African coast opposite Spain, and then eastwards through Algeria to Tunisia. The available specimens in the British Museum and the collection of Col. Meinertzhagen suggest that, east of the type-locality, *witherbyi* and *lavaudeni* are inseparable, and Hartert's decision to merge *lavaudeni* with *witherbyi* is therefore accepted. Further west, a transitional population is involved, and it is possible that a small proportion of transitional specimens also occur east of the type-locality.

In Tunisia, the form *witherbyi* is indistinguishable from *melophilus* in plumage, though the two populations are a thousand miles apart and there is a population of different colour in between. This situation recalls that of the two separated *rubecula*-like populations already mentioned. However, in the present case, the wing-length of *witherbyi* is smaller than that of *melophilus*, and the difference seems sufficient to justify subspecific separation. The culmen of *witherbyi* is not smaller than that of *melophilus*, and may even be very slightly larger.

As already remarked, typical *rubecula* breeds in northern, eastern and central Europe. The breeding Robins in Portugal and central Spain have a rather darker and more orange breast than typical *rubecula*, but the back is as grey as in the latter form. In southern Spain and in North Africa opposite Spain, the breast is rather deeper in colour, and this trend of variation (cline) is continued eastward into Algeria until typical *witherbyi* colour is attained. At a later stage in this cline, the back starts to become more olive. Birds from Portugal were at one time referred to *melophilus* and birds from southern

Spain to *witherbyi*, but both are distinguishable from *melophilus* or Tunisian *witherbyi* by their grey backs. From central Spain to eastern Algeria, the Robin population is best designated as *rubecula* ≥ *witherbyi*.

It is interesting that, although *melophilus* and *witherbyi* are alike in plumage, the populations transitional with *rubecula* are distinguishable. This is because in the cline from *rubecula* to *melophilus* the back-colour changes before the breast-colour, and in the cline from *rubecula* to *witherbyi* the breast-colour changes before the back-colour. Hence *rubecula* ≥ *melophilus* tend to be comparatively olive-backed and pale-breasted, while *rubecula* ≥ *witherbyi* tend to be comparatively grey-backed and dark orange-breasted.

Most authorities, (e.g. Ramsay, 1923) describe *witherbyi* as having a breast of the same colour as *melophilus*, but upper parts closer in colour to those of *rubecula*. This, of course, really applies to the transitional population, and is due to the fact, already mentioned, that the type-locality of *witherbyi* is not at the far end of the cline, where the upper parts are similar in colour to those of *melophilus*. Under these circumstances some workers might prefer to retain *lavaudeni* Bannerman for the Tunisian birds, and to designate the Algerian birds as *rubecula* ≥ *lavaudeni*. This procedure is less confusing than that adopted here, but as *witherbyi* was named before *lavaudeni*, the former must have priority if specimens from the type-locality of *witherbyi* cannot be adequately separated from those of *lavaudeni*, as seems the case.

Inland in Morocco, the breeding form of the Robin does not apparently form part of the *rubecula* ≥ *witherbyi* cline, but shows a reversion to a comparatively grey-backed, pale-breasted form indistinguishable from typical *rubecula*, and hence representing another 'island' of the latter form. E. Mayr writes that the large series of Moroccan birds in the American Museum of Natural History is indistinguishable from typical *rubecula*. Some specimens in the British Museum (Natural History) collected by Chaworth-Musters (1939) in February near the western end of the High Atlas are, if anything, even greyer on the back and paler on the breast than typical *rubecula*; from the date, these specimens could conceivably have been European migrants but this seems unlikely (migrants are said to keep to the coast), and Robins were later found breeding in the locality in question. Lynes (1924), who named the form *atlas* from the Middle Atlas Mountains, considered this form close to *witherbyi*. However, he was evidently comparing it with transitional *rubecula* ≥ *witherbyi* (see previous paragraph). Possibly he collected in an area where 'Moroccan-*rubecula*' intergrades with the main Spanish-Tunisian *rubecula-witherbyi* cline.

I have not seen specimens of *E. r. sardus* Kleinschmidt, which breeds in Corsica and Sardinia. According to Hartert (1910), this form differs from typical *rubecula* in being more olive-brown above and almost as orange-red below as *melophilus*. If this is correct, then this population may be another one transitional between typical Continental *rubecula* and Tunisian *witherbyi*, which would accord with the geographical position of Sardinia and Corsica.

Migration

Robins breeding in northern Europe winter in southern Europe and North Africa. Wintering *rubecula* from the Continent have also been reported in the Atlantic islands, and in Corsica. Likewise some British Robins migrate to the Pyrenees. Again, Continental *rubecula* arrive on the east coast of Britain in autumn, and though most of these individuals pass on, some possibly stop the winter; this at least is the opinion of Dr J.M. Harrison, though it is difficult to be certain, as breeding specimens from the extreme east of England are sometimes rather pale on the breast, like *rubecula*. As yet, no Robin ringed on the Continent has been found in Britain, and none ringed in Britain in winter has been found on the Continent.

The existence of migration makes it difficult to be sure that any particular collected specimen belongs to the local breeding form, except for those taken when actually breeding, at which season the plumage is worn, so that colours are less clear than at other seasons, and the primaries are often too frayed for reliable measurement. Owing to these doubts, I have not given average wing-measurements in this paper, as they might be misleading, but I have indicated where I think that there is a difference in size.

So far as known, the *rubecula*-like Robins breeding on Madeira, the Azores, and the western Canary Islands do not migrate, and it is most unlikely that they would do so. On the other hand, typical *rubecula* from most of Finno-Scandia are wholly migratory. There is, therefore, an ethological difference between these two *rubecula* populations. In Finland, the Robin is wholly migratory, though an occasional bird stays as late as December, only to die during the winter (Palmgren, private communication). In Norway, the Robin is wholly migratory except for a few wintering in the comparatively warm south-western coastal region (Collett, 1921). In East Prussia, a very few Robins winter regularly, though dying if the weather is unusually severe (Tischler, 1940). From East Prussia southward and westward, an increasing proportion of Robins are non-migratory. Hence the zone of intergradation between wholly migratory and wholly non-migratory Robin populations is extensive, and greater than that occupied by the extremes.

The subspecies concept

The taxonomic genus is a convenient unit for cataloguing related species. The taxonomic species has real validity and also great practical convenience. But the taxonomic subspecies or geographical race presents serious difficulties, both logical and practical. Formerly this concept was of great value, as it drew attention to the existence of geographical variation within the species. Further, it worked well when birds had been collected only from discrete regions each of which was well separated from the next, and it still works well for many insular or otherwise isolated forms, such as *superbus* in the case of the Robin. But when, as now for the Robin, the subspecies concept is applied to extensive collections made over a large land area, the practical difficulties become considerable, many judgements are inevitably arbitrary, and the use of subspecific names, so far from helping, actually becomes misleading as a description of the type of variation.

First, the use of separate names implies a degree of separation between populations which often does not exist. The 'British' Robin is not, in fact, completely 'British' in the east of England, and is perhaps most 'British' of all in Ireland, while Continental Robins from Holland have 'British leanings'. In general, subspecies usually intergrade with each other, and this may be represented, as in the present paper, by writing the two subspecific names with a linking sign. But the transitional population thus designated is not a uniform one, and this terminology does not reveal that one character may change in a different way from another, e.g. in the region between typical *rubecula* and typical *melophilus* the back becomes more olive before the breast becomes more orange. Further, the transitional zone may be extensive, perhaps more extensive than that occupied by one of the end forms, and the use of the terminology of subspecific transition then becomes clumsy. Under these conditions, some workers may prefer to give the transitional population a different name, e.g. *caucasicus* instead of *rubecula* $\gtrless$ *hyrcanus*, but this at once conceals the intermediate nature of the form in question.

Another difficulty concerns the type-locality for subspecies. The type-locality of *melophilus* is in Hertfordshire, which is perhaps just far enough west to avoid the pale-breasted variants sometimes found in eastern England, though it must be near the border. It would have been easier if the type-locality had been further west, but the type-locality was determined not by considerations of variation in the Robin, but by the accident of where the Rothschild family happened to settle. In the case of the Algerian Robin *witherbyi*, the accidentally determined type-locality has led to serious difficulty, as it would have been preferable to have had a name for the Tunisian breeding form, which represents the end of a cline. This accidental fixing of type-localities for subspecies will constitute an increasingly difficult problem as trends of variation become better known. Yet the provision of type-localities is essential.

The use of subspecific names not only implies discontinuity where none may exist, but also unity where there may, in fact, be discontinuity. Thus the breeding Robins of the Azores (and Madeira) bear the same subspecific name, *rubecula*, as those of Scandinavia, though the two populations are isolated from each other by a population of different appearance. In the parallel case of the Tunisian and British Robins, the two populations receive separate names because, though alike in plumage, they happen to be separable in measurements. Now there is also a difference in measurements in the case of the Azorean and Scandinavian populations, but in this case it happens not to be enough for subspecific separation. Yet, though not sufficiently separable by their appearance, the Azorean and Scandinavian Robin populations are discrete units, and the situation is obscured by giving them the same name. There is a third 'island' of *rubecula*-like birds in the Atlas Mountains. Again, the provision of separate subspecific names for the Tunisian and British Robins, which on some grounds is desirable, hides the fact that these two populations have similar plumage.

The arguments brought forward by Huxley (1938) as to the inadequacy of subspecific terminology apply, with added force, to the case of the Robin. Huxley's concept of clines, which is intended to supplement subspecific description, represents a marked advance. However, difficulties of the type raised for the Robin will, I believe, be found to apply to many other species when intensive collecting has been carried out in all parts of the range. One therefore begins to wonder whether subspecific trinomial terminology is not beginning to outlive its usefulness and validity. Certainly, in the case of *Erithacus rubecula*, it is both simpler and more accurate to describe subspecific variations in terms of geographical trends, and to omit altogether the tyranny of subspecific names.

Summary

1. The Robin or Redbreast, *Erithacus rubecula* (Linn.), is so close to the Bluethroats and Nightingales that there is probably a case for sinking the genus *Luscinia* into *Erithacus*. *E. rubecula* is not particularly close to the Japanese Robin *L. akahige*.

2. *Erithacus rubecula* is here divided into five subspecies, *superbus* Koenig on Gran Canaria and Tenerife, *hyrcanus* Blanford in Persia, *witherbyi* Hartert in eastern Algeria and Tunisia, *melophilus* Hartert in most of Britain, and *rubecula* (Linnaeus) in northern, eastern and central Europe, also in the Azores, Madeira and Western Canary Islands, and in part of Morocco. A possible sixth race, *tartaricus* Grote from the Urals, was not examined.

3. The subspecies *rubecula* intergrades with *hyrcanus* in the Caucasus, with *witherbyi* in southern Iberia and part of North Africa, and with *melophilus* in the districts bordering the North Sea and English Channel. These transitional populations have sometimes received separate names.

4. The races *witherbyi* and *melophilus* are alike in plumage, though living 1000 miles apart, with a form of different colour in between. The transition from *rubecula* to *melophilus* occurs in a different way to that from *rubecula* to *witherbyi*.

5. The breeding birds on the Azores and other Atlantic islands cannot be differentiated subspecifically from those of Scandinavia, though separated by a population of different colour in between.

6. The situation is confused by the migration of more northerly forms into

regions where more southerly forms reside.

7. The provision of subspecific names confuses, instead of assisting, the description of the subspecific variations found in *Erithacus rubecula*.

Acknowledgements

I am much indebted to the authorities at the British Museum of Natural History (J.D. Macdonald) and to the Rijks Museum v. Nat. Historie at Leiden (Dr G.C.A. Junge), also to Dr J.M. Harrison and Col. Meinertzhagen, for giving me every help in studying their collections. I am also indebted to Lt-Col. Tenison and Capt. Grant for some valuable criticisms, and to Dr E. Mayr, who provided information on specimens in the American Museum of Natural History, and who also helped greatly by criticising the manuscript in draft.

References

Chaworth-Musters, J.L. (1939) Some notes on the birds of the High Atlas of Morocco, *Ibis*, pp. 269–70, 277.

Collett, R. (1921) *Norges Fugle*, i, p. 71.

Grote, H. (1928) *Erithacus rubecula tartaricus*, nov. subsp. *Orn. Monatsb*, xxxvi, pp. 52–3.

Grote, H. (1929) S. Buturlins Neubeschreibungen aus dem nördlichen Kaukasusgebiet, *Falco*, xxvi, pp. 21.

Harrison, J.M. (1942) A Handlist of the birds of the Sevenoaks or western district of Kent, pp. 67–70.

Hartert, E. (1910) 'Die Vögel der Paläarktischen Fauna,' i, pp. 732, 742, 750–5.

Hartert, E. (1922) *Idem.*, iii, pp. 2168–9.

Hartert, E. (1928) 'A rush through Tunisia, Algeria and Marocco, and collecting in the Maroccan Atlas, in 1927.' *Novit. Zool.*, xxxiv, pp. 361–2.

Huxley, J.S. (1938) 'Clines: an auxiliary taxonomic principle', *Nature*, cxlii, p. 219.

Jahn, H. (1942) 'Zur Oekologie und Biologie der Vögel Japans', *Journ. f. Ornith.*, xc, pp. 185–7.

Lebeurier, E., and Rapine, J. (1936) 'Ornithologie de la Basse-Bretagne', *L'Oiseau*, n.s. 6, pp. 252–71.

Lynes, Rear Admiral (1924) 'An ornithological visit to NW Marocco (Spanish province of Yebala)', *Novit. Zool.*, xxxi, pp. 81–2.

Ramsay, R.G.W. (1923) *Guide to the Birds of Europe and North Africa*, p. 138.

Seebohm, H. (1881) 'Catalogue of the Passeriformes or perching birds in the collection of the British Museum', **Cichlomorphae**, Pt. II. Catalogue of the Birds in the British Museum, v. pp. 292–312.

Tischler, F. (1940) *Die Vögel Ostpreussens*, p. 461.

Witherby, H.F. *et al.* (1938) *The Handbook of British Birds*, ii, pp. 199–204.

Note The above works include reference to all the **other** important papers on the taxonomy of the Robin not cited specially.

A review of some recent researches, with remarks on the possible outcome of the present intensive racial survey of British birds

Mr P.A. Clancey read the following paper [at the meeting on 19 June 1946]:

This is the first opportunity I have had of addressing the British Ornithologists' Club, and it is my intention to review some of my recent researches into certain species of birds and then to visualise the racial map of Britain as it will appear on the completion of the comprehensive survey which I have in mind.

Perhaps the most interesting discoveries have been confined to the Paridae. Here it is becoming increasingly evident that a strong tendency to local variation is finding expression in some interesting inconsistencies in the distribution of established races. For instance, it is now known that *Parus palustris dresseri* Stejneger is confined to the southern potion of the species' range in Great Britain, the northern type being somewhat similar to near Continental forms, either *P.p. stagnatilis* Brehm or *P.p. longirostris* Kleinschmidt. I am still collecting material with a view to further research, and a paper on the subject will be prepared in due course.

The finding of specimens of a Cole Tit approaching *Parus ater hibernicus* Ogilvie-Grant in the coloration of the nuchal spots and cheeks, in parts of west and north-west Scotland, is a discovery of some importance. As is already well known, birds resembling *P.a. hibernicus* are found in parts of South Wales, while in County Down, Northern Ireland, birds resembling our British race *P.a. britannicus* Sharpe and Dresser, are found. A great deal of collecting is clearly needed before this racial problem can be elucidated.

The validity of Prâzak's *Parus caeruleus obscurus* has never really been in doubt, but recent surveys of series from many parts of Britain have shown that this species is likewise strongly influenced by local factors, and I have succeeded in locating some three variations: two from England, tending to pallor and brightness of plumage, and one from Scotland, confined to the northern portion, exhibiting a tendency to darkness of the mantle.

The Great Tits of the British Isles have been receiving attention recently, and there is no need for me to go over what is already in print and available to all, but I do think a few more words on the question of the birds from northern Scotland will not go amiss. In the *Bulletin* for 1945, I suggested that the bird from this region might possibly be *Parus major major* Linnaeus. I have recently acquired further material, and it now appears that the bird of this region is intermediate in bill structure and plumage coloration between

P. m. major and *P. m. newtoni* – a rather similar case to the one of East Anglian intergrades recently discussed by Dr J.M. Harrison. I have not followed up Mr Jeffery Harrison's very interesting account of south-western Scottish Great Tits, but feel sure that an examination of specimens from some of the Inner Hebrides would help to throw additional light on the question of a crassirostral west Scots form. The Island of Arran in the Firth of Clyde is a place of prominent importance in the study of western Scottish races, and Great Tits from there should be of some significance. As will be seen from these illustrations, the Paridae present an enlightening picture of local variations of structure and plumage coloration, and I feel confident that further concentrated study of the British Group will add much to our know-ledge of evolutionary change in the more incipient stages.

The British races of the Chaffinch, and particularly the question of the validity of *Fringilla coelebs scotica* Harrison, 1937, have been discussed in a variety of notes, and I have quite recently reviewed the entire position and attempt to define the ranges of the forms occurring in our area. *F. c. gengleri* Kleinschmidt ranges throughout England, Wales and Ireland, overlapping *F. c. scotica* Harrison in south-east Scotland and *F. c. coelebs* Linnaeus in the East Anglian littoral. A closely allied but paler and brighter form is found in northern Scotland, and is entirely severed from the southern British race by a broad belt of *F. c. scotica*, which occurs throughout Scotland, south of the Grampian massif. It seems evident that the northern Scottish Chaffinch has, in a good many individuals, acquired racial criteria which would normally justify its accession to subspecific rank, but many are, however, like *F. c. gengleri*, and so the position is confused. A modification of the trinomial system of nomenclature should be devised to meet intricacies of this sort. A similar case is to be found in the distribution of *Chloris cloris* races in Great Britain. Studies into other members of the British Fringillidae should prove equally instructive, but few of them are so widely distributed throughout these islands as the two species just mentioned. I am hoping to be in a position to make a statement on British Goldfinches (*Carduelis*) before the end of the year. As for the Hawfinch (*Coccothraustes*), I do not expect we will find much in the nature of local variation in Great Britain because the species is still extending its range northward. In the case of the Bullfinch I have found a belt of intergrades between *Pyrrhula pyrrhula nesa* Mathews and Iredale and *P. p. coccinea* in the coastal areas of east Suffolk and Essex. *P. p. coccinea* has not hitherto been recorded in this country; it is a good form, but only really separable from *P. p. nesa* in the female.

These remarks on the Fringillidae will, no doubt, bring to your minds other species likely to be influenced by local factors. The Wren (*Troglodytes*) has been subject-matter for a considerable number of my ornithological communications. It is evident that the Wren in Britain is splitting up into a coterie of closely connected forms, or sub-races, and that the range of *Troglodytes troglodytes troglodytes* (Linnaeus) is gradually shrinking as the local

106

variations become more accentuated. Some of the colour differences are extremely fine, and can only be perceived in extensive series and after painstaking study. It may be that at some future date most of the British islands will possess their own named races of Wren, but at the present time it is evident that no further forms should be separated under name until a truly exhaustive material is available from the entire area to be covered. I am attempting something in the nature of a review for the species in continental Europe, but the material needed is vast and that available extremely meagre. Another species which has received attention recently is the Redbreast (*Erithacus*), and it has now been firmly established that a good many from extreme north of Scotland are darker, more earthen brown, above than *Erithacus rubecula melophilus* Hartert, some approaching closely the Continental race. Dr Harrison has already indicated that some Redbreasts from southeast England exhibit similar tendencies. The colour cline of *Erithacus rubecula melophilus* reaches its apogee in western Scotland, and the interesting northern bird just described has been formed doubtless by an intergradation between this and the typical race from Scandinavia.

Here I must end my rough survey of recent racial researches – by no means the entire field covered, but highly illustrative of the type of work which is being carried out at the present time. I have not gone into points raised in my numerous notes and papers on western Palaearctic races, with which you are all well acquainted. It will be appreciated that I have had little time to pursue all channels of enquiry undertaken before and during the early part of the War, but it is my earnest desire to right this at the earliest possible opportunity. The amount of collecting which remains to be carried out before anything resembling a complete review can be undertaken is quite enormous. Careful map-work and planned collecting are the only methods by which many of the gaps in our available material and knowledge can be narrowed or closed.

I now come to what can loosely be described as the peroration of this short address – an attempt to try and visualise the possible outcome of the present racial research work into British birds.

For a considerable time now evidence as to the heterogeneity of the British mainland birds has been accumulating apace, and it is now clear that many areas support distinct forms (local variations) in varying stages of separability. For your guidance I will list the areas I have in mind, viz. north Scotland, that is Scotland north of the Grampian system; south-west Scotland – with its strong Hebridean influences; south-west Ireland; Salisbury Plain; the littoral of south-east England – an area of pronounced continental racial penetration. All these regions require much further study before theories are advanced as to the influences at work.

The question 'How, with available names, can all these local variations be recognised?' will at once come to mind. Mr C.W. Mackworth-Praed dealt with the question in summary manner, and suggested an alteration in our nomenclature in *The Ibis* for 1943, but left much unanswered, while Dr Harrison (1945) advanced still another modification of the trinomial system of zoological nomenclature, whereby forms based on slender criteria could be accorded recognition in scientific literature. As matters stand at present much of inestimable value is liable to slip into obscurity unless some modification or other of our present system of nomenclature is brought into use with the least conceivable delay. Of course, there is the view that the variations of which I speak can be given due recognition by the system as it stands at present, and in support of this contention I would here express the view that these variations are not necessarily less distinct than the bulk of named forms in continental Europe. I have always been strongly of the opinion that the validity of a form should rest solely on the measure of constancy of its imputed criteria and not on degree of separability. Races named on fine distinctions are considered as equally valid as those separated on extremely salient and palpable racial characteristics, because to ignore the former type can only result in one thing – complete and utter chaos. The ignoring of fine forms was followed in the *Handbook of British Birds* with amazing thoroughness and with most unsatisfactory results. We cannot compel Nature to accept the dictates of recognised scientific procedure, but must so modify our system of nomenclature that all types of races can be accorded due recognition.

To return to more friendly territory; let us consider one or two of the difficulties which stand in the way of a speedy recasting of the entire racial layout in Britain. Many type-localities of British races are still undecided – nowadays a pinpoint fixation is needed. A type-locality, such as England or South England, can seriously hamper research. A case in point is that of *Totanus totanus britannicus* (Mathews); the author of this race made the cardinal mistake of not giving a definite type-locality fixation. I agree there were difficulties in the way at the time which barred a fuller study of the entire question – but rushing into print can have its complications. *Totanus totanus britannicus* is now a race without a really definite type-locality. Dr Harrison has suggested South England, but I have seen breeding birds from the eastern marshes of England which are certainly not representative of *T. t. britannicus*, as understood by the late Dr Ticehurst. It is quite evident that a more precise fixation is called for. There are several other cases, but I will not deal with them here.

Old names in the synonymy are also a source of trouble; it is often not clear if they are merely substitute names for something already known or if the authors intended them to signify something recognised as distinct. A descriptive case is that of the *Fringilla Linota* of Latham, to which I have already referred in an earlier note. I am not in favour of resuscitating dubious names if a means by which they can be left dormant can be found.

The first essentials are, therefore, the careful fixation of type-localities and elimination of unwanted names. Once this has been accomplished the recasting can be started. I feel confident that in a few years' time much of the edifice we know so well at present will have changed, and instead of one name covering all the divergent chromatic and structural variations now evident in these islands, we will have a series of carefully named races with due recognition accorded to overlaps and penetrations of Continental influence. The recent work on Skylarks is illustrative of this prognosticism – Witherby in 1938 recognised no British races; in 1942 I supported *Alauda arvensis scotica* Tschusi, and suggested others existed. In 1946 I separated *Alauda arvensis tertialis*, from the Salisbury Plain, Wiltshire, England. Before many years have passed the Hebrides, Ireland, North Scotland, etc., will, I believe, support their own named races of Skylarks. Similar tendencies are perceptible in other groups with which we are all conversant.

In ending this short address I would like to express the wish that we all face the changes around us with good grace, realising that the antithesis of progress is stagnation, and without progress finality in any science, if at all attainable, cannot possibly be achieved.

Mr H. N. Southern then made some observations and has supplied the following note:

The following remarks amplify the query I raised as to the number of specimens upon which Mr Clancey's proposed races were based.

The description and naming of groups within a species involve a very different procedure from the description and naming of separate species. The fundamental nature of this difference does not seem to have been appreciated by recent systematic work in this country.

When one is dealing with systematic groups such as species, between which breeding is exceptional, the variation in the sum of the characters considered is *discontinuous*. It is, therefore, permissible to name and describe a new species from only a small amount of material, on the assumption (usually justified by subsequent information) that the characters described will be valid for the whole of the inter-breeding group concerned.

With subspecies, however, the matter is more difficult. Since one is dealing with groups that inter-breed (isolated subspecies must be considered as potentially inter-breeding), in most cases variation within the group is *continuous*, although the rate of change may not be constant for a given geographical distance. Thus, to take an extreme case, if a species is characterised by a steady increase in size of bill from one end of its range to the other, single specimens from each end will nearly always be separable. For any shorter distance, however (and consequent smaller range of difference), the chance that a single individual will not represent the mean for its neighbourhood becomes important. Thus it is quite possible that a small number of specimens obtained from two localities might show an apparent reversal of the general trend, since each sample would be too small to give a proper picture of the distribution of variation in one locality.

It is, in fact, improbable that in a size gradient or cline of this type the mean measurement will increase at a constant rate per mile (if this were so it would obviously be impossible to describe and name any subspecies), and therefore groups of sufficient individuality to receive a subspecific name will exist. It will, however, be impossible to distinguish with precision the boundaries of such groups except by the application of simple statistical methods: these require samples of a definite magnitude, according to the total range of variation being considered within the group. Though the minimum size of sample required will vary in this way, it is safe to say that it will always be much higher than the numbers Mr Clancey has used.

This illustration has used the character of size for the sake of simplicity. Naturally the same argument applies to variation in colour, although this is more difficult to measure. However, such measurements of colour have been carried out on Deer-mice, and there is no reason why the method should not also be applied to birds.

The description of intra-specific variation can often be summarised by naming subspecies, but there are many cases where this cannot be done. Under present systematic procedure such kinds of variation have to stay undescribed, and this must remain so until some kind of adjustment is made.

Mr B.W. Tucker then made some observations, of which the following is the gist (but some points have been amplified or added):

Mr Clancey's researches raise points of much interest and emphasize the fact – certainly not novel to the more biologically-minded systematists – that the situation with regard to geographical variation in an area such as the British Isles may be a good deal less simple than was once supposed. The existence of areas in south-east England and elsewhere in which the populations of various species, or a certain proportion of individuals, agree or intergrade with long recognised Continental races is now seen to be not an exceptional and aberrant phenomenon, but one of widespread occurrence, which must be allowed due weight in any objective treatment of racial forms in the British Islands. At the same time we are getting evidence that apart from these Continental or quasi-Continental types, the populations of a number of species are less uniform over the whole area of Great Britain than was formerly assumed. The views and suggestions which Mr Clancey has put forward with regard to these local variations merit close and unprejudiced consideration.

Nevertheless, I feel it is necessary to offer some words of warning on the subject. New ideas or methods in taxonomy, as in any other branch of science, should clearly not be rejected merely because they conflict with established procedure, or appear to do so, but neither should they be uncritically accepted merely because they are proclaimed to be 'modern', or because their merits are vigorously asserted by their authors.

Facts such as those to which we have had our attention drawn tonight reveal an evolutionary situation much more interesting than was implied by the assumption of uniform 'British races' over at least the whole mainland of Great Britain, but also one of such complexity as to demand the employment of all the possible weapons of modern biological research if any real progress is to be made in its study.

I am sure Mr Clancey will forgive me if I say that one danger which I see lies in a certain complacency in his approach to the whole subject, and in the implication that all this work is extraordinarily 'progressive', and that those who may be disinclined to accept all his conclusions are mere obscurantists or too old-fashioned to appreciate the significance of these 'modern' developments. Now, in actual fact, it is, I believe, a serious weakness of researches of this kind in this country that they are themselves not sufficiently 'up-to-date' in their approach, and are pursued with so little apparent awareness of the conclusions and methods of the more progressive systematists abroad, as well as of what I may call the broader biological background of the subject.

The most important work of the kind I have in mind emanates at present from America. It so happens that one of the most important and constructive contributions to evolutionary literature in recent years is the work of an ornithologist, Ernst Mayr, of the American Museum of Natural History. Mayr is not only the leading authority on the systematics of the birds of the East Indian and Pacific islands, as I need hardly remind this company, but also outstandingly well informed on the work of systematists in other fields of zoology than his own and on what I have called the broad biological background of modern systematics. His book *Systematics and the Origin of Species* (Columbia University Press, 1942) contains much that is relevant to the topic of this evening.

Another outstanding work bearing even more directly on the subject under discussion is A.H. Miller's *Study of Speciation in the Avian Genus Junco* (University of California Publications in Zoology, 1941), a really masterly treatment of just the type of problems we are concerned with tonight, using all the apparatus of modern systematic techniques. I earnestly commend these two works to all who are interested in the modern biological approach to systematics, and I would go so far as to say that no one is qualified to make any real progress in the subject who has not read and thoroughly digested their contents.

The whole subject is one of such extent and complexity that it is impossible to review at all adequately in a brief extempore communication of this kind at the end of one of our meetings, but let me direct particular attention to one point which must be already present to the minds of many of you – I mean the designation by trinomial names of ever finer and finer geographical variants of more and more restricted distribution.

Mr Southern has already called attention to the need for proper statistical treatment of proposed new races. I can, therefore, pass over this important consideration and concentrate on another point to which he has already briefly alluded, namely, that whereas in the higher vertebrates, species, with relatively few exceptions, are perfectly clear-cut entities, the recognition and definition of which is usually a comparatively simple and straightforward matter, the subspecies is something much less objective and less clearly defined. The defining and naming of subspecies is a weapon for facilitating the study of geographical variation within the species, but if it is carried to exaggerated lengths there is a danger of the whole system collapsing under its own weight, or being reduced to futility and defeating the very object for which it was established.

It may be said that much the same sort of argument was put forward against the trinomial system itself in its early days, but I believe that whereas it was quite unjustified in that connection it is very much to the point at the present time and in the present context.

I will give you my reasons for this view. It is a fact that wherever organisms have been sufficiently intensively studied, as in the case of the Deer-mouse, *Peromyscus*, the Fruit-fly, *Drosophila*, and certain kinds of snails, it has been found that *any local population can be shown to be genetically different from any other*, provided only that the technique of analysis is sufficiently delicate and precise. If, then, a demonstrable difference is to be the only criterion, the logical and unavoidable conclusion which follows from this demonstration is that – at least in the case of fairly sedentary birds – names should ultimately be given to the populations of every moderately isolated area of woodland, moor or marsh. It is merely a matter of the delicacy of the analytical technique applied to them. This is a *reductio ad absurdum* of the practice of attempting to name ever smaller and smaller and less clearly isolated units. In the nature of the case a halt has got to be called at some point, and I suggest that the point should be that at which such multiplication of names begins merely to confuse and retard the study of geographic variation, and further that no subspecies ought to be considered even tentatively valid which does not conform to the statistical criteria mentioned by Mr Southern and cannot be assigned a reasonably clearly defined area of distribution in which its characters are approximately constant. It may be a much truer representation of the facts of nature to say that a certain subspecies shows a tendency to be a little greyer in this area or a little browner in that than to attempt to cut it up into finer named subspecies with the implication of more or less clear-cut divisions which in fact have no reality.

Lest anyone should take exception to the views I am expressing, on the grounds that I am merely a biologist interested in systematics and not a working systematist, I will quote just two passages from Mayr's book.

In some of these groups, as for example Palaearctic and Nearctic birds, even most of the 'good' subspecies are already described, and a phase of excessive splitting has been reached. New subspecies are described because the means of the measurements differ by a few per cent or because there is a very slight difference in the tone of general coloration. The populations on which such 'subspecies' are based are admittedly genetically different from others of the species, but to name them is impractical since it obscures rather than facilitates the presentation of the facts of intraspecific variation.

Or again,

The terminology of the taxonomist, designed for practical purposes, is always an idealization and represents the facts as simpler than they are. The nontaxonomist and the beginner amongst taxonomists will save themselves much trouble if they realise this situation fully. Not even the most extreme splitting will ever lead to completely homogeneous categories.

It is indisputable that Mayr is one of the most progressive and able of modern taxonomists, and these passages could hardly be more apposite to the present discussion. I could quote others, but the two will suffice.

I realise, of course, that when I say that the giving of trinomial names should cease at (or before) the point when it merely confuses the issue and becomes a nuisance there will be differences of opinion as to where this point lies. But the trouble at present is that some taxonomical enthusiasts are not sufficiently aware of the biological facts which I have just put before you to realise that the necessity for finding some such practical solution of the problem exists.

Again, I should like it to be to clearly understood that the considerations I have put before you are offered as general propositions in connection with the problem of intra-specific differentiation. At the moment I am not specifically criticising any one, or necessarily criticising any, of the local forms to which Mr Clancey has given names, for I have not had the opportunity of investigating them sufficiently critically, but I do say emphatically that the critical evidence needed to defend them has not been brought forward so far.

To get back to the main problem of the multiplication of 'micro-subspecies', if several subspecies are to be recognised within the relatively insignificant area of the mainland of Great Britain, what must be the situation with species which range over a great part of the vast area of Continental Europe and Palaearctic Asia? I gather that Mr Clancey thinks that, at any rate with some of the species he has studied, the uniformity over a large part of Continental Europe is relatively much greater than for some reason it is in Great Britain. But even supposing this to be so, it is quite beyond belief that in the immense areas to which I have alluded there are not a very great number of local populations as much entitled to distinction as some of Mr Clancey's British races. And so, if his views are to be followed, we must visualise the eventual naming in each of a large number of widely distributed birds of hundreds of subspecies, mostly with small and very uncertainly

definable ranges and doubtfully identifiable on the basis of individual specimens. Such a situation would be a stultification of the whole principle of
trinomial nomenclature.

It is, of course, well known that in continuous land areas not subdivided
by natural barriers such as mountains or deserts the ranges of different
subspecies are not sharply defined; they are separated by zones of intergradation. This is just what we should expect, because the populations are not
isolated from one another. But seeing that such transitional zones between
subspecies are of normal occurrence, owing to the interpenetration of populations at their borders, how is it conceivable that such a relatively small and
little isolated area as, say, Salisbury Plain, can be sufficiently free from interpenetration of this kind to maintain a population at once sufficiently distinct
and sufficiently uniform to deserve the status of a named subspecies? Such a
situation is so inherently improbable that a claim to that effect requires to be
supported by much more comprehensive evidence than Mr Clancey offers
us.

In conclusion I would like to repeat that I regard the facts which Mr
Clancey's studies are revealing as of great interest. They certainly deserve the
closest investigation, but I am certain that they demand a much more critical
approach than we have yet seen in this country. The issues we have been
discussing this evening are serious ones, which have got to be faced by scientific ornithologists here if we are not to lag behind our friends in America and
elsewhere, floundering in a morass of mere names, the employment of which
for small and ill-defined local populations I believe to be downright
misleading and, if persisted in, likely to retard progress in the study of the
phenomena of local variation rather than to advance it.

It may be that a modification of current taxonomic procedure *can* be
found to cover fine local variation without doing violence to the facts of
nature: or it may be, as I myself am convinced, that trying to define local
populations by trinomial names, or definite labels in any form, has gone
about as far as it can go in western Europe without defeating the objects of
the trinomial system, and that a quite different technique is needed. But as a
preliminary to a new approach to the whole problem, we should at least
recognise where an over-enthusiasm for mere rule-of-thumb naming of local
forms may lead us, lest we find ourselves acquiescing in the development of a
system of such complexity that no one can cope with it, with no compen-
sating advantage in the better understanding of the facts of geographical
variation.

In defence of the principle of the 'first revisor'

by Dean Amadon

From vol. 75 (1955): 21–3

In the *Bulletin of the British Ornithologists' Club* (vol. 74, No. 7, October 1, 1954), Captain C.H.B. Grant* has attacked the principle of the 'first revisor' in problems of nomenclature, citing as an example of this supposedly pernicious practice the efforts by Dr James P. Chapin and myself (Ostrich, 1952, p. 123) to preserve the name *philippensis* for the Spotted-billed Pelican. It frequently happened among the older ornithological writers that descriptions of several new species, often poorly characterised, were given in quick succession in the same work. Some of these descriptions are identifiable, others are not. The names that can be identified have been in use, often for decades. Later, however, it sometimes happens that a researcher, with greater or lesser justification, believes that he can identify some of the names that have hitherto been regarded as unidentifiable. If such a name happens to have page or line priority over a name that has been in general use, and if line priority is sustained, the well known name that has been in general use will be displaced. To prevent this kind of disturbing change in scientific names, the International Committee on Zoological Nomenclature has taken the position that all the names appearing in a single publication are to be regarded as having appeared simultaneously, that is, page and line priority does not affect the availability of names. But it often happened that the same species was inadvertently described several times under different names in

---

*Captain Grant was an indefatigable resuscitator of old scientific names which in his opinion took precedence over later and better-known ones. The following verse, and accompanying note, is quoted, with permission, from B.P. Hall and Derek Goodwin's *Bird-room Ballads*.

The Law of Priority

> *I'm a raker-up of muckheaps*
> *And my name is Captain Grant.*
> *I'm greatly pleased if I can find*
> *Forgotten names, long left behind*
> *By saner folk, and if I can't*
> *Revive the lot, my name's not Grant.*

B.P.H.

Most of the more personal ballads have been left out of the selection. This one is included in affectionate memory of one who never refused help or advice to the younger members of the staff but never minded if they disagreed with him and positively enjoyed it if they pulled his leg.

the same publication. To handle such situations, the principle of the *first revisor* was drawn up; it states that of several equally available names, the one selected by the first subsequent revisor is to be retained even though some other name applying to the same taxonomic entity is later shown to have page or line priority. The principle of the *first revisor* was temporarily jeopardised by the Paris Zoological Congress in 1948, but, following much opposition to this retrogressive action, the more recent Copenhagen Zoological Congress returned to the previous acceptance of the *first revisor* principle (Copenhagen Decisions, 1953, Art. 28, pp. 66–7).

With this preamble, let us now consider the pelicans! Gmelin, in his edition of the *Systema Naturae* (1789) briefly described three pelicans. *Pelecanus roseus, P. manillensis,* and *P. philippensis.* Bonaparte, in his *Conspectus,* concluded that all three names apply to the Spotted-billed Pelican; he used the name *philippensis,* perhaps because he regarded its identity as more certain, with *roseus* and *manillensis* as synonyms. Thereby he acted as *first revisor.* The name *philippensis* was subsequently used for this species in the British Museum's *Catalogue,* in Peters' *Check-list,* in Stuart Baker's *Fauna of British India,* etc.

On the other hand, the name *roseus,* because Gmelin's description did not tally very well with the Spotted-billed Pelican, was subsequently used for a species supposed to be very closely allied to the Roseate Pelican, *Pelecanus onocrotalus* Linnaeus, but differing from it by being slightly smaller and by having 22 instead of 24 tail feathers. Even Peters listed *Pelecanus roseus* as a separate species. Most authors assumed that it was, at best, no more than a subspecies of the Roseate Pelican. Chapin and I (*op. cit.*) were dubious that the form *roseus* is valid in any sense and suggested keeping *onocrotalus* as a monotypic species, although, admittedly, more material from eastern Asia needs to be examined.

The name *Pelecanus roseus* of Gmelin has as type locality Manila, as do the other two pelicans named by him at the same time. Since there is no record of the Roseate Pelican from the Philippine Islands, Mackworth-Praed and Grant (1934, *Bull. Brit. Orn. Club,* 55: 63–5) decided that *roseus* must, after all, refer to the Spotted-billed Pelican. (Actually the description, as already mentioned, does not agree very well with that form and there is no reason why Roseate Pelicans could not occasionally wander to the Philippines from the coast of Indo-China where they nest, or from elsewhere.) Mackworth-Praed and Grant went further and stated that since *roseus* has page priority over *philippensis,* the former name must displace the latter. This conclusion runs counter to the principle of the first revisor and is erroneous. Nevertheless, as so often seems to be the case, the change was accepted with undue alacrity by the authors of several important recent works, even though it meant replacing the established name *Pelecanus philippensis* not merely by another name but by one whose association in the literature with a form allied with the Roseate Pelican could only lead to confusion. It was for this

116

reason that Chapin and I stated that if no other means of saving the name *philippensis* were at hand, we would be in favour of petitioning the International Commission to have it set up as a *nomen conservandum*. But the clear restatement of the principle of the *first revisor* at Copenhagen makes such recourse unnecessary. Incidentally, Captain Grant is scarcely justified in suggesting that this principle hinders the *taxonomic* revisions of the systematist, rather it merely forms one point in the Rules as they affect *nomenclatorial* revisions (of which the fewer the better!).

One may add that the tenor of the discussions on nomenclature as published in the preliminary Copenhagen decisions leaves no doubt that taxonomists will be well advised to heed the increasingly insistent clamour of other biologists against all avoidable changes in scientific names. Otherwise, the matter may be taken out of our hands, as has already been attempted by certain groups in applied botany, who have set up a list of names of their own.

The British list

The Ibis and British Birds are the main journals in which additions to the British list, and the evidence on which they are based, are published and discussed. As the following extracts show, the Bulletin has made some contributions. It published records of the first breeding of two rare grebes. There was a detailed account of how the recently 'discovered' British Willow Tit differs from the Marsh Tit. Many of the controversial 'Hastings Rarities' were published in the Bulletin, a few of which are included here; and there, was some early discussion of the question of 'assisted passages' and introductions.

First recorded breeding
of the Slavonian Grebe in Britain

From the report on the Club's meeting on 16 February 1910.

Mr W.R. Ogilvie-Grant recorded the first undoubted instance of the Slavonian Grebe (*Podicipes auritus*, Linn.) breeding in Great Britain, and exhibited a fine adult example in full breeding-plumage, which had been shot on a small highland loch in Inverness-shire in the beginning of June 1908. By the desire of the owner of the bird, he was prohibited from mentioning his name or from supplying further particulars. Mr Ogilvie-Grant said that he was indebted to Mr Hugh M. Warrand for obtaining the loan of this interesting specimen and for enabling him to establish this record, which would otherwise have remained unpublished. Mr Warrand had supplied the following notes:

> The year before last, in the beginning of June, I obtained permission for myself and a friend to fish on a small reedy sheet of water in the hills of Inverness-shire.

119

The day being very warm and bright, few fish were rising, so we landed and lay down by a rock on the shore. While waiting there I observed some bird moving among the reeds near us, and presently noticed that it was swimming round a pile of green reed-stalks like a Coot's nest. At first I thought it was a Coot, but when it came into full view I noticed the peculiar head with its sweeping crests of buff, and knew that it was a bird that I had not seen before. I called the attention of my friend and also of the keeper to it, and we all observed it for some time swimming restlessly about the nest among the reeds and evidently longing for our departure. I regret to say that the next time I saw this Grebe it was lying dead in a bird-stuffer's shop, and I was told whence it had come and who had brought it – facts which have since been fully corroborated. I had hoped that it would have been left in peace to establish a family, and greatly deplored its death. I was cheered, however, to learn the following year (1909) that one or two pairs had appeared on the same loch, but soon afterwards heard that the nests had been ruthlessly robbed by a private egg-collector.

Mr Ogilvie-Grant said that the Slavonian Grebe had been said to nest on some freshwater lochs near Gairloch in Ross-shire, but that according to Mr A.H. Evans the identification was incorrect, and the birds were the Little Grebe (*P. fluviatilis*) (cf. *Ann. Scot. N. H.* 1892, p. 171). There is also some evidence that it bred in Benbecula in 1893; two were shot in full summer plumage in Barra in April 1898 (*t.c.* 1903, p. 21); and one at Arisaig, Inverness, on the 13th of May, 1907 (*t.c.* 1908, p. 207).

* * *

Despite this initial setback, the Slavonian Grebe has become an established, if rather rare, British breeding bird. Its range is based in the Highlands of Scotland where about sixty pairs breed, down from a maximum of about eighty pairs a decade ago.

A. G. KNOX

First recorded breeding of the Black-necked Grebe in England

Black-necked Grebes first bred in Britain in Wales from 1904, and then at the Tring Reservoirs in several years between 1918 and 1928, but not there since. Up to 1970 no more than ten pairs nested each year in the whole of Britain, since when there has been a slow increase to a maximum of 37 pairs in the late 1980s.

A. G. KNOX

From the report on the Club's meeting on 11 December 1918.

Mr Chas. Oldham gave the following account of the nesting of the Black-necked Grebe in Hertfordshire:

The Black-necked Grebe (*Podiceps nigricollis*) has appeared from time to time on the large canal-reservoirs at Tring, but, apart from an adult in full breeding dress on April 18th, 1909, it was until the spring of 1918 looked upon as an irregular and uncommon winter visitor. In Lord Rothschild's collection at Tring are three birds, all in winter plumage:

Date	Sex	Age
Nov. 24th, 1903	M	Adult winter plumage
Nov. 19th, 1908	F	Young of year
Nov. 21st, 1908	F	Adult winter plumage

Besides these four birds I have notes of one on November 5th, 1911, one, which I judged from some slight differences in plumage to be another bird, on December 2nd of that year, and one on January 20th and 27th, 1918.

On April 28th, 1918, I noticed two birds in full breeding plumage, obviously from the slight difference in size a pair, swimming in close company on one of the reservoirs, and it was with a very lively interest that my sister-in-law, D., and I saw them again at the same place on May 4th and 14th, for their sojourn suggested that possibly they would settle down and nest. Three days later D. saw four birds, and on the 21st a party of seven – three pairs and an unattached male. I had these seven birds under observation for some hours on the 26th. For the most part they fed in close proximity – indeed, at times a blanket would have covered the whole party – but now and then a pair would detach themselves from the others and go off on a short cruise. Essentially sociable as the birds were, the odd male was treated with some intolerance, for at times one of the others made a rush at it as though to drive it off. That the birds, although paired, should at the end of May maintain this close association and spend hours together fishing in the open water was puzzling, for although from the first there had been indications of nuptial display – of which more hereafter – there was nothing to suggest that nesting had actually begun, and at the breeding-place described in 1904 by Mr O.V. Aplin (*Zoologist*, 1904, pp. 417–20), which is now generally known to be in Wales, young are often hatched at the beginning of June.* The association

*Mr Aplin records two pairs with young on June 3rd and five pairs with young a few days later in 1904. In 1907 there were newly hatched young at this Welsh breeding-place on May 18th, and on June 15th of that year a bird nearly as large as an adult. Broods are not, however, all hatched out at the same time, for on June 21st, 1910, there were four broods, varying in size from newly hatched to half-grown birds.

that had obtained during the second half of May did, however, break down at the end of the month, for on June 1st the three pairs were feeding in different parts of the reservoir, whilst the unattached male was cruising alone, and after that date we only saw the birds singly or in pairs. By June 6th a pair had moved to one of the other reservoirs, and later in the month another pair frequented the place for a day or two. On the 26th D. saw two birds, not mates apparently, fishing at some distance apart on this water. One of them went repeatedly into a thick bed of *Typha*, always at the same spot, behaviour which the head keeper noticed too on the 29th. The inference was that the bird was feeding a sitting mate, or more probably newly hatched young, on the nest. The reservoirs are fringed in places with broad dense beds of reeds and *Typha angustifolia* – admirable nesting-places for Grebes – and, although the keepers by Lord Rothschild's orders were on the look-out for nests, it is hardly a matter for surprise that none was seen, for the recesses of the reed-beds could only have been explored at the risk of disturbing the birds.

On the last day of June a pair and an unattached bird were swimming in open water on the reservoir which the whole party had frequented during May. Even at a considerable distance one of this pair looked much more bulky and sat higher in the water than its mate, and I suspected that it was carrying young. This suspicion was strengthened when its mate swam towards it with food in its mouth and passed the food to something on its back. With the telescope we could plainly see the heads of young ones protruding above the raised wings of the bulkier bird, but it was impossible to tell at the distance how many young there were. Once during the two hours we were at the place a single young one swam clear of the parent for a minute or two and then clambered up again over its tail. Except for a few brief intervals the other parent was constantly bringing food to the young, diving in the shallow water close to its mate. It stayed under water for only a few seconds at a time, and so achieved several journeys per minute; indeed, its industry and activity were astonishing compared with the more leisurely tactics of the Great Crested Grebe when feeding young. Although I never ascertained how many young were hatched out by this pair – it is certain that there was more than one chick on the back of the old bird on June 30th – it may be that only one was reared, for in the latter part of July I could never detect more than one, with an old bird always in close attendance. On August 11th, by which time it was well grown, this young bird was fishing on its own account, and I could see nothing of either parent.

Four days after our first sight of this brood D. saw a pair with newly hatched young on the other water, at the edge of the *Typha*-bed and close to the spot where she had seen the bird go in on June 26th. We spent some time watching this pair at close quarters on the afternoon of July 6th. The three chicks were carried on the back of one parent and fed in that position by the other, which came at frequent intervals with a small fish held crosswise in its bill. Now and then on the approach of the old bird with food a chick would slide into the water from the back of the nursing bird, only to regain its cradle quickly by climbing up over its tail. Once the bird that was carrying the young shook them off its back and dived. They swam immediately to the other bird, clambered up over its tail, and the roles of the old birds were reversed. A fortnight later the division of labour still obtained, but its mode had changed, for then one parent had sole charge of two and the other of one of the clamorous and apparently insatiable chicks, each party feeding independently of and at some distance from the other. On August 4th the young birds were diving and fishing to some extent on their own account, but most of the food was still caught by the old birds. By August the 11th the young, which were then about two-thirds the size of the old birds, were scattered about the reservoir and seemed to be quite independent of parental control. A week later I could find neither old nor young, and can only conclude that all the birds left the neighbourhood as soon as the young could fly, a proceeding in striking contrast with that of the Great Crested Grebes, which do not leave the reservoirs for the winter until the latter part of October. That two pairs nested and reared broods is beyond question. It may be that the third pair nested, but escaped notice – an easy matter if the total acreage of the reservoirs is taken into account; but after the party broke up at the beginning of June little was seen of this pair or of the unattached bird.

As few people in this country have any first-hand acquaintance with the Black-necked Grebe in its nesting haunts, some extracts from my notebooks regarding the appearance and behaviour of the birds may not be out of place.

In life the silky yellow ear-coverts are not folded closely as represented in most figures, but, radiating from a centre, occupy a third of a circle and show as golden rays against the black cheeks. In conjunction with the upstanding frontal crest, the tip-tilted bill, and crimson eye, they contribute not a little to the bizarre appearance of the bird. The young for the first few days are much darker in colour than Great Crested Grebes of the same age and resemble young Dabchicks, but the stripes on the neck and body are more obscure than in either. At four weeks the stripes on the body are imperceptible and those on the neck difficult to make out, even with a glass, at a distance of a few yards. The birds are then dark ash-grey with fore-neck, breast, and cheeks white, and at a little distance look like young Coots rather than Grebes. Their rate of growth is astonishing. A couple of days makes a perceptible difference in their size and at six weeks they are more than two-thirds the size of the adults. The rate of growth in the Great Crested Grebe, and I think the Dabchick too, is much slower. The curious habit that Grebes have of protruding and wagging a foot behind them is practised early in life, for several times we saw a young one do so whilst on the old one's back.

Before nesting actually began there was evidence that the Black-neck engages in nuptial displays akin to those of the Great Crested Grebe, but unfortunately the performance which Mr J. Huxley (*P.Z.S.*, 1914, pp. 491–562) calls a 'shaking bout', although often observed, was always engaged in at too great distance for details of pose and of the disposition of the plumage to be appreciated. Mr Aplin (*loc. cit.*) refers to a bout between two birds that had a young brood, and such a thing may be not uncommon; it certainly is not in the case of the Great Crested Grebe. On May 19th a bird – I think, a male – brought to the surface what looked like a piece of matted alga, and swimming up to its mate proffered the morsel, an action probably connected with courtship, whilst on May the 21st, D. saw two of the birds 'stand up in the water on their tails, facing one another and shaking and bowing their heads,' a performance obviously analogous to the 'penguin-dance' of the Great Crested Grebe described by Mr Huxley.

The paired birds usually kept close together, but sometimes when fishing they became separated and would then call to one another with a plaintive *pee-eep*, a note which Naumann (Nat. Vog. Deutschl. vol. ix, pp. 768–84, 1838) renders *beeb*. That author describes as *bidder, vidder, vidder, vidder*, another note which is very like the rippling cry of the Dabchick, though lacking perhaps something of its trill. In Wales I have heard a harsh creaking note strongly reminiscent of the call of the Partridge, and probably the analogue of the groaning croak which the Great Crested Grebe utters in the spring. The alarm-note resembles the *whit* of the Dabchick, but it is neither so loud nor so sharp. The hunger-cry of the young, uttered incessantly as they follow the old birds for food, is similar in general character to that of the Great Crested Grebe, which Mr W.P. Pycraft (*The British Bird Book*, vol. iv, p. 427) aptly renders as *pee-a, pee-a, pee-a*, and of the Dabchick, but is not quite like either. The difference, although difficult to express in words, was apparent enough when the young of all three species were calling at once in close proximity. The hunger-cry of the Dabchick is shriller and more quickly iterated than that of the Great Crested Grebe and lacks something of its querulous tone.

When feeding, the birds are more under water than on the surface. Half-a-dozen dives in deep water, not consecutive but taken at random, timed 25, 26, 23, 27, 28, and 26 seconds respectively, but in shallow water and particularly when the old birds are feeding young the duration is often much less. So far as I could judge the young were fed exclusively on small fish, but when old enough to forage for themselves they took other food as well. They picked something, apparently small insects, from the surface of the water, and on one occasion one brought from the bottom what looked like a large drowned earthworm and swallowed it.

The birds evinced little fear of people walking on the reservoir banks and merely swam out for a few yards if anyone passed when they were feeding close inshore. When encumbered with a brood this indifference was even greater, and they would feed the young ones with apparent unconcern, although people were standing and watching them at a distance of a few feet. I was standing one afternoon at the water's edge looking at an old bird with two young ones. On two occasions this bird came to the surface just at my feet. It did then evince some alarm, uttering a cry, *whit, whit, whit,* it rushed through the water for a yard or two with body submerged and head and neck only protruding, then dived again just as the Great Crested Grebe does under similar circumstances. This discomposure was, however, only momentary, and the bird resumed the even tenor of its fishing without more ado.

If, as seems likely, the birds come to Tring again next year, they will be secure from molestation in the protection of Lord Rothschild. One can only hope that if any take up their quarters on other waters they will enjoy a like immunity and that collectors will refrain from taking either birds or eggs until they have had a chance of properly establishing themselves, for, putting on one side the interest which they have for the academic ornithologist, these curious and very beautiful Grebes would be a welcome addition to the regular avifauna of our inland waters.

* * *

Lord Rothschild said that from statements made to him by the head keeper (James Street), that he distinctly saw on Wilstone Reservoir two pairs of these Grebe with young and one pair on Marsworth Reservoir, he was convinced that all three pairs of birds successfully hatched and brought up their young.

British Willow Tit

The Club's meeting on 9 November 1932 was devoted almost entirely to the Willow Tit *Parus montanus*, which was at last beginning to be fairly well known, at least to some perceptive field workers. It was only in 1897 that it was realised that the Willow Tit occurred in Britain as well as the Marsh Tit *Parus palustris*. Three years later it was described as *P. m. kleinschmidti*, a form not very different from those that occur in the adjacent Low Countries. Witherby followed Hartert in treating the Palaearctic Willow Tits as conspecific with the rather similar North American Black-capped Chickadee *P. atricapillus* (a name that had priority over *montanus*), but for a number of good reasons it later became clear that this was a mistake and the Old and New World birds should be treated as separate species, as in fact Hellmayr did when he described the British Willow Tit.

As an extenuating circumstance, partially excusing the failure of British ornithologists to discover the Willow Tit, it may be mentioned that Marsh and Willow Tit are far more similar to one another in Britain than they are on the Continent, except in the Low Countries; in Scandinavia, for instance, as H.G. Alexander notes, they cannot possibly be confused.

From the report of the Club's meeting on 9 November 1932.

Mr H.F. Witherby exhibited a series of skins of British and Continental Willow-tits (*Parus atricapillus*) and Marsh-tits (*Parus palustris*), as well as a nesting-cavity and nest of a British Willow-tit and diagrams of nesting cavities, and made the following remarks:

In 1900 Dr Hellmayr described the British Willow-tit, taking as the type a bird collected at Coalfall Wood near Finchley, and then in the Tring Museum Collection. This type, with others, has now gone to New York, but we may hope that some day it may be returned to us.*

Dr Hellmayr named the bird *Parus montanus kleinschmidti*, after the well-known German ornithologist, who had already discovered, from specimens which he had found amongst Marsh-tits in the British Museum, that we had a Willow-tit in this country.

The naming of a British bird after a German ornithologist was a shrewd blow at us, but one which we thoroughly deserved, since no British ornithologist either in the field or the museum had detected the presence of the Willow-tit in this country. Moreover it remained unrecognised, except by a few, for a long time after Dr Hellmayr described it.

In 1907 in the first number of *British Birds*, i, 1907, p. 23, the late Dr P.L. Sclater wrote an article on the British Willow-tit, referring to it as a 'supposed' new British Tit. A little later Lord Rothschild wrote describing the bird's distinctions, and deploring the want of its recognition, and we attached an editorial appeal for observations.

The first serious contribution on the notes and distribution of the bird from field observations was made by the late C.J. Alexander (*British Birds*, iv, 1910, pp. 146–7), who worked with his brother H.G. Alexander who, I am glad to see, is here tonight. Since then a good many observations have been made, but by comparatively few. We now have a general idea of the bird's distribution and a fair idea of its habits, but there is much more to be learnt.

I make no excuse for bringing the subject forward here for these reasons, and also because there are still a good many who do not know the bird and are doubtful of its distinctions, and some who definitely refuse to believe there is such a bird.

This summer [1932], on May 28, a keeper pointed out to me a Tit's nest in a hole in a tree on the borders of Wilstone Reservoir, near Tring. The hole had evidently been bored by the bird itself, and was in a small rotten willow

*It was returned.

126

overhanging a wide ditch along a marshy field and separated by a narrow pathway from the reeds on the edge of the reservoir.

The bird sat tight, then went off the joined its mate. It was difficult to see them well, but from glimpses I got I thought they were Willow-tits, and this was confirmed by a deep toned 'tchēē-tchēē' alarm note uttered twice. But the birds were on this occasion very undemonstrative, and they were no doubt incubating.

Lord Rothschild having kindly given me permission to make a full investigation of the nest I visited it again on June 4. On this occasion I was accompanied by Mr E.M. Nicholson, whom we have here tonight.

We had perfect views of the birds, which were feeding young with beaks full of small flies. They were very demonstrative and constantly shivered their wings and uttered a string of alarm notes chiefly 'tchay' repeated several times, a deep-toned note. Sometimes it was distinctly 'tchēē', and was occasionally prefaced by a very high-pitched 'zit', which seemed to come at the height of their excitement at our presence. At one time the old birds were in such a perfect light, at close range a little below the level of our eyes, that the crowns appeared to both of us, at different angles, as obviously a deep sooty colour, and at no time could we see any gloss on them. A pale edging to the secondaries was observable once or twice, but was a difficult feature.

We made an entry into the back of the nesting-hole and extracted one nestling for examination. This was one or two days old, with some pin-feathers but none yet broken out. I wrote down a description of the down plumage and mouth coloration, and this does not differ from the Marsh-tit.

On June 11 I visited the nest again and watched the birds feeding the young, this time with green caterpillars. The young were now nearly ready to fly.

As carefully collected material of the birds in this stage was much wanted I took the young and collected one old bird, and am showing these here tonight, and also the nesting-hole and nest.

It is well known that Willow-tits bore their own nesting-holes, but I am sure there is a good deal more to be learnt about the shape and size of these cavities. I have brought up for exhibition the Tring nesting-hole, and Mr Musselwhite has kindly brought one in a birch, which he took some years ago, and from which he caught the bird which was identified at the Natural History Museum as a Willow-tit. I have made rough diagrams and taken measurements of these two cavities. You will see that they are both retort-shaped like the cavity made by a Woodpecker. It seems to me very remarkable that the Willow-tit with its feeble little beak should bore out a hole shaped like those of the Woodpeckers – birds to which it bears no relation. It must have very soft rotten wood, and it evidently cannot overcome obstacles such as hard pieces. You will see a hard knot in the Tring nest which has quite spoilt the symmetry of the hole. And perhaps the harder wood on the entrance side has driven it too far over, so that it came against the hard bark on the other side. Mr Musselwhite's nest is a more perfect example, but it seems probable that Willow-tits's nesting-holes vary in size according to the nature of the wood. Even in Mr Musselwhite's example the bird has not been able to make a correct-shaped entrance probably owing to hard bark.

Mr H.G. Alexander contributed the following notes on Willow- and Marsh-tits. He said:

I do not think I can add to what is generally known about field identification of the Willow-tit by sight. Of the various features that might be mentioned – blackish-brown head instead of glossy black, buff underparts and whitish patch on the secondaries – the last-named, the pale wing-patch, is, to my mind, the only infallible one. The colour of the crown seems to vary very much in different lights, and the Marsh-tit sometimes looks fairly buff on the sides, though I rather think its throat is a purer white; this point struck me again only last week, when I saw both species on one day.

But unless I see the colour of the closed wing well, I dare not identify the bird for certain if it is quite silent.

As I believe the notes and plumage are supposed by some sceptics to vary at different times of year, I have been through my notes for the past 25 years, and I find that in 24 years of fairly regular observation I have seen Willow-tits in every month of the year, though for some reason less frequently in May and June (14 years and 10 years respectively, out of the 24) than in any other month. I think this is partly because I am not much interested in birds' nests, but chiefly because the song-period ends early.

Actually, the Willow-tit's very sweet, almost canary-like song, is uttered very erratically through the year. In this respect I would compare it to the Pied Wagtail. I find that in the course of 24 years I have heard the song in every month – only once each in June and November, and only twice in October and December. In March I have heard it in 11 years, in April in 16 years, but in May only in 4 years. But it has a rather strong period of song in late summer, for I have heard it in 7 years in July, 11 in August, and 9 in September.

This contrasts rather curiously with the Marsh-tit, whose song-period (I refer to the loud single note repeated it may be a dozen times or more) is much more clearly marked. In 22 years of observation I have heard the Marsh-tit's song every year in March and April, in 15 years in February and May, and in 14 Januaries. For the rest of the year the number is much lower, and I have only heard it in 3 Septembers.

As to the call-notes, these, of course, are numerous with all the British Tits (except perhaps Long-tailed). Just as Great and Marsh are sometimes almost indistinguishable, so, too, the Willow sometimes utters uncertain notes. But it is quite as easy to confuse some of its notes with Blue as with Marsh.

The two commonest notes, however, are really very distinct. One is about the highest, thinnest little note of any British bird I know, except for the little Bat-like note which a Lesser Whitethroat sometimes utters. It is this note which can sometimes be confused with a half-note (if one may use such an expression) of a Blue-tit. The second note, a very deep, 'charr, charr, charr', is right at the other end of the scale, and is very much har her than any note a Marsh-tit makes. It is, to my mind, one of the most arresting call-notes of any of our small birds. It is as startling as the scolding note of the Dartford Warbler.

As a rule, I hear and see Willow-tits in hedges or small copses, often in places quite a long distance from woods – in fact, in places where one would not expect to see a Marsh-tit.

I might perhaps mention, in conclusion, that the Central European subspecies, in Holland and Germany, seem to be distinguishable in nearly the same way as our birds. But I was amused to discover that in Norway, where I again found the two species living side by side, they seemed almost to have exchanged liveries. It was clear enough, both to ear and eye, that two species were present; but the Willow-tit is there much the paler species, and the whitish secondaries are inconspicuous.

Northern Willow Tit

From the report of the Club's meeting on 18 November 1908.

Mr Ogilvie-Grant exhibited a specimen of the Northern Marsh-tit (*Parus borealis* (Selys-Longch.) which had been shot by Mr J.H. Paddock at Tetbury, Gloucestershire, in March 1907, and made the following remarks:

Mr Paddock, who has taken considerable interest in the question of the Marsh-tit and the Willow-tit, has presented examples of these birds to the British Museum. Among them he has forwarded the present example of *P. borealis*, which is a north-west European species and has not hitherto been recorded from Great Britain.

In connection with the occurrence of this interesting accidental visitor, I should like to quote from part of a letter written by myself to Mr H.F. Witherby:

When I was at Welwyn in Hertfordshire last Sunday (12th of January, 1908), I saw a small lot of Marsh-tits of sorts which interested me vastly. I was first attracted by the note (song), which was unknown to me, and sounded like that of a Linnet. I got quite close to one of them; it was perched on a thorn-bush about ten yards off. There he was, a Marsh-tit *singing* a Linnet-like song! There was no room for doubt. So far as I could see, he was rather a pale-looking bird, and perhaps a trifle more robust than our Marsh-tit (*P. palustris*): the sides of his face were conspicuously white, and his flanks were pale like the breast. I have never seen the Scandinavian Marsh-tit alive, but that was what he reminded me of. I know the Common Marsh-tit's notes as well, or better than most people do, but I never heard that species give vent to a little broken ascending song with different notes. There were four or five birds in company, and two were singing as described. If not the Scandinavian Marsh-tit, what could the birds have been? Have any of your correspondents met with a similar experience?

As I have not been able to secure a specimen for identification, I did not wish to place my observations on record, but now that Mr Paddock has forwarded an undoubted example of this species there can be no reason why *P. borealis* should not be added to the list of accidental visitors to Great Britain.

The specimen mentioned here constitutes the first (and still only) fully acceptable record of the largely sedentary Northern Willow Tit *P.m. borealis*. The later sight record is regarded as probable rather than fully proven.

A.G. KNOX

Purple-headed Starlings in the British Isles

This is another example, on a much larger geographical scale than the case of the Irish Coal Tit, illustrating the difficulties of applying subspecific names to individuals in populations with wide, continuous ranges, especially if there is also migration. Dr Alan Knox comments that *Sturnus vulgaris poltaratskyi* has not been accepted on to the British list, largely for the reasons given here by B.W. Tucker. Dr C.J. Feare comments as follows:

> I think that all we can say is that there is no hard evidence that the race *poltaratskyi* has occurred in the British Isles. However, ring recoveries suggest that birds originating almost as far east as the Urals have been recorded in Britain and, as the zone of overlap between *poltaratskyi* [which breeds in Siberia, west to the Urals] and *vulgaris* is somewhat woolly, it may well be that some purple-headed birds from west of the Urals could reach Britain. There are, of course other purple-headed forms, especially around the Caspian Sea and it is also possible that some of these birds, which are also migrants, could occasionally reach our shores. It is important to emphasise that the distinctions between the various subspecies of Starling are subtle and they could not be distinguished in the field.

From the report on the Club's meeting on 16 May 1945.

Mr Jeffery Harrison exhibited a specimen of a Starling with a purplish head which he shot in Lincolnshire on December 23, 1943 (*British Birds*, xxxviii, 1944, p. 112). The bird was ultimately identified as an example of *Sturnus vulgaris poltaratskyi*, an eastern race of Starling. He made some further remarks on the subject, which led to an interesting discussion.

Dr James Harrison made the following remarks upon *Sturnus vulgaris poltaratskyi* Finsch as a British bird, and the occurrence in the British Isles of possible intermediates between this form and *Sturnus vulgaris vulgaris* Linnaeus, also a record of *Sturnus vulgaris poltaratskyi* from Italy:

Since the first record of *Sturnus vulgaris poltaratskyi* (*British Birds*, xxxviii, pp. 112, 113) by Jeffery G. Harrison, from the mouth of the River Witham, near Boston, Lincolnshire, on December 23, 1943, a survey of several hundred British-taken examples of *Sturnus vulgaris* has been made. The review of this material has revealed no fewer than four individuals whose characters depart sufficiently from those of the typical form to merit analysis. One of these, a male, is a true *Sturnus vulgaris poltaratskyi*, and was obtained at Otford, near Sevenoaks, on March 19, 1928 [the other three, of intermediate character, are then described].

The detection of *Sturnus vulgaris poltaratskyi* in Lincolnshire and Kent, and the appearances of the other two intermediate examples from Kent, rendered it desirable to pursue this matter further, and to this end I have had a number of Starlings specially sent me from the east coast during this spring – samplings from flocks. A batch of six received included one obtained on March 20 at Northcotes, Lincolnshire, which proved on examination to be a further example of *Sturnus vulgaris poltaratskyi*. It was one of a small flock within 2½ miles of the sea-wall. This example is a male, the plumage is still spotted, the gonads were minute and it was somewhat fat. The bill had commenced to turn yellow in its centre, while the base of the lower mandible was grey. The reflections presented by this specimen are as follows: Forehead and crown purple, nape and mantle green, rump green, upper tail-coverts green. The ear-coverts are green, the chin and whole of the throat purple. The breast is green, merging to a bluish-black belly, while the flanks are blue-purple. The wing-coverts are green. The under wing-coverts and axillaries are pale sepia edged with pale cinnamon buff.

It may not be out of place here to refer to a small series of Starlings I collected in Thrace and Bulgaria during 1932 and 1935 (*vide Ibis*, July and October 1933 and July 1937). This region in Europe would appear to be a meeting place for a number of different forms, and the status of this species was discussed in the papers referred to above, and it is to be noted that I have in my collection an adult male example of *Sturnus vulgaris poltaratskyi*, collected on March 17, 1929, near Florence, Italy. It is clear that the species group *Sturnus vulgaris* Linnaeus demands much systematic study before its complexities can be satisfactorily resolved.

Miss E.P. Leach exhibited the mummified body of a Starling found in a bombed shop in Putney High Street in the first week of October 1944, having probably died in the previous winter, and which appeared to agree in its characters with *Sturnus vulgaris poltaratskyi*. This was a ringed bird and was trapped as an adult in a garden at Wimbledon on May 31, 1939. Miss Leach also showed a specimen from Bickleigh, S. Devon, January 30, 1945, which had been ringed at Leiden, Holland, and also appeared to show these characters to a lesser extent.

Mr B.W. Tucker made the following remarks (in abstract) on these birds and others exhibited by him:

The Putney bird was kindly sent to me by Miss Leach for examination. It agrees with *Sturnus vulgaris poltaratskyi* in the purple, instead of green, gloss on the crown and also in the purplish flanks, which seems to be a *S. poltaratskyi* character, as against a more steely blue colour in *S. vulgaris*. On comparing this bird with the quite small series of Starlings in the Oxford University Museum, I found another British-killed specimen which, apart from a slight difference in the degree of wear of the plumage, is absolutely identical with it. This was shot at Windsor in, according to the label, April 1895. It appears to me highly improbable that the very small series of British-killed Starlings at Oxford should include another Siberian specimen, and the date when the Putney bird was ringed suggests, though it does not prove, that it was breeding in this country. These considerations cannot fail to raise some doubt whether these purple-crowned birds are correctly identified as *S. poltaratskyi* and whether they are not more likely to be variants of the typical race which resemble the Siberian race more or less closely. The latter alternative seems to be strengthened by the fact that specimens with crowns of a somewhat intermediate type can be found amongst birds from the British Isles and Western Europe. On the other hand the Windsor specimen is in surprisingly unworn plumage for April and heavily spotted, which, in view of Bullough's work on the Starling, might suggest that it *is* a foreign bird. There is a possibility, however, that the date is incorrect.

The fact that purple-crowned birds occur in the British Isles is not a new discovery. Indeed, Mr Kinnear has kindly drawn my attention to the fact that it was discussed by Bowdler Sharpe (*Catalogue of Birds in the British Museum*, vol. xiii, p. 29) as long ago as 1890. Sharpe expressly describes these birds as intermediate between *S. vulgaris* and *menzbieri* (=*S. poltaratskyi*), but states that in his experience they are 'never true *S. menzbieri*, as they always have green ear-coverts' instead of purple. This last point applies also to the birds now under discussion, both the Putney and Windsor specimens having ear-coverts with a greenish, not purplish, gloss. It will be seen, therefore, that Sharpe had already recognised most of the essential facts in the situation which is now attracting renewed attention. It may be doubted, however, whether the colour of the ear-coverts is such a valid difference as Sharpe supposed between 'true *menzbieri*' or *poltaratskyi* as we now call it, and the British birds. Hartert in describing *poltaratskyi* does not go further than to say '*more or less* purple ear-coverts' (my italics), and I have today examined in the British Museum series birds shot in Sind in winter, which are generally accepted as *poltaratskyi* (and in any case are not *S. vulgaris*), in which the ear-coverts are definitely greenish.

We therefore arrive at the position that there occur in the British Isles, at any rate in winter, and apparently not very uncommonly, Starlings which, on the basis of a preliminary examination, do not appear to differ decisively from *Sturnus vulgaris poltaratskyi* in any character. Nevertheless, I am not convinced that this race should be added to the British list, for the reasons already given. A very important point, which remains to be determined by the study of a really adequate series, is whether purple-crowned individuals occur regularly amongst definitely breeding birds in Britain and, if so, whether the proportion is about the same as in winter. Pending a more thorough investigation the above remarks must be regarded as essentially preliminary and provisional.

Colonel Meinertzhagen said:

Not only Sharpe but Dresser, Hartert and Witherby recognised that British Starlings frequently had purplish heads. In my key to the Starlings, after having examined the large series of *S. v. poltaratskyi* in Leningrad, I found that the purple ear-coverts were a constant character in breeding birds from Siberia, in the same way that green ear-coverts are a constant character in British breeding birds. The mantle of both these races is green. But where you get British purple-headed birds the purple is not pure violet-purple as in *S. v. poltaratskyi*, but with a slight admixture of oily green. I have recently shot British breeding birds with purplish heads, notably in the Scilly Isles, Berkshire and Norfolk; and in my collection of several dozen British Starlings a large proportion have purplish heads, but in every case green ear-coverts.

Mr Jeffery Harrison's bird more closely resembles true *S. v. poltaratskyi* than any British-taken Starling I have seen, for the ear-coverts are distinctly purplish, but that does not follow that it is a migrant from Siberia.

Supplementary note by B.W. Tucker:

The general upshot of the discussion at the meeting, and especially of Col. Meinertzhagen's observations, has been very strongly to reinforce my opinion that in the present state of the evidence, and pending an exhaustive investigation, with special reference to British breeding birds, it is altogether undesirable and imprudent to assume that purple-crowned Starlings obtained in Western Europe are Siberian immigrants, and to record them as such.

It is evident from what we have heard that more work will be required to determine what these purple-headed Starlings now turning up in England really are. Sharpe, as Colonel Meinertzhagen and Mr B.W. Tucker have already pointed out, more than fifty years ago described what was apparently the same thing as intermediate between *S. vulgaris* and *S. menzbieri* (=*S. poltaratskyi*) and suggested they should be named. This was never done, and it is remarkable that this question should crop up again now, after half a century. G.C.L. (Editor)

The Hastings Rarities

Around the turn of the century and for the following two decades there was an extraordinary series of claimed records of rare birds, of which these are just a few, from Kent and Sussex. Most passed through the hands of George Bristow, a taxidermist of St Leonards-on-sea, and collectively they became known as the 'Hastings Rarities'. Following an extensive review published in 1962, sixteen species including Black Lark, thirteen subspecies (including Large-billed Reed Bunting) and hundreds of other records were struck from the British list (*British Birds*, 55: 281–384; see also J.M. Harrison, 1968, *Bristow and the Hastings Rarities Affair*, privately published). The 'Hastings Rarities' are still regarded as thoroughly discredited*, although some of the taxa have since been reinstated on the basis of different records.

A.G. KNOX

From the report on the Club's meeting on 18 June 1902.

Mr W. Ruskin Butterfield exhibited a specimen of *Saxicola caterinae* [*Oenanthe hispanica*], Whitaker, shot in Sussex. This is the Western form of the Black-eared Chat (*S. aurita*, Temm.), and although a more or less common breeding species in southern Europe, it was not known to have previously visited the British Isles.

---

*Dr J.M. Harrison never accepted that they were fraudulent, partly because he could not believe that M.J. Nicoll, whom he knew well, would have been a party to such a deception. He was working on a sequel to his book on the subject up to the time of his death.

The specimen, a male, had been shot by a man named Williams, near Polegate, Sussex, on May 28th, 1902. It had been received for preservation by Mr George Bristow, of St Leonard's, and examined in the flesh by Mr Butterfield.

From the report on the Club's meeting on 20 May 1903.

Mr W. Ruskin Butterfield exhibited a specimen of the Black-headed Wagtail, *Motacilla feldeggi* of Michahelles, which had been shot near Willingdon, Sussex, on May 13th last, and examined by himself in the flesh and in fresh condition. The specimen had been compared with the series of *M. feldeggi* in the British Museum, and there could be no doubt that it was rightly identified. It was a male in fine plumage. The species was not known to have previously occurred in the British Isles.

Mr Butterfield also exhibited two males of the Grey-headed Wagtail, *Motacilla borealis*, Sundev., procured on the same day and near the same place. One of these specimens had been handled in the flesh, and the other (a somewhat damaged bird) shortly after it had been skinned. They presented slight differences, both in coloration and in the length of the bill and claws, but Dr Bowdler Sharpe and Mr Butterfield had found no difficulty in matching them with examples of *M. borealis* in the British Museum series.

From the report on the Club's meeting on 17 January 1906.

Mr Ruskin Butterfield exhibited a specimen of the Wall-creeper (*Tichodroma muraria*) which had been shot while climbing about the face of the cliff at Ecclesbourne, near Hastings, on the 26th December, 1905. The bird – a female – was taken to Mr G. Bristow, of St Leonards, and was shown by him to Mr Butterfield before it was skinned.

Three previous occurrences of this bird in England had been made known, namely: (1) An example shot at Stratton-Strawless, Norfolk, 30th October, 1792 [cf. Marsham and White, *Trans. Norf. and Norw. Nat. Soc.*, ii, pp. 180, 184, 188 (1876)]; (2) an example obtained at Sabden, Lancashire, 8th May, 1872 (cf. F.S. Mitchell, *Zool.*, s.s., p. 4839); (3) an example, now in the collection of Canon H.B. Tristram, shot at Winchelsea, Sussex [cf. Sharpe, *Bull. BOC.*, vi, no. xxxviii, p. 8 (1896).] Professor Newton, (*Dict. B.*, p. 986, footnote,) had called attention to the fact that Merrett had included the species in his list of British birds in 1667, the passage being as follows: 'Picus murarius, *the Creeper, or Wall-creeper, I. ib. Ald.*, i, 852. G. 644.' (*Pinax Rerum Naturalium Britanicarum*, 1667, p. 177.)

From the report on the Club's meeting on 20 February 1907.

Mr C.B. Ticehurst exhibited a male and a female of the Black Lark [*Melano-corypha yeltoniensis* (Forst.)], a species new to the British avifauna, and made the following remarks:

The male, which was in company with another male and two females, was shot by Mr Sargeant at Sewers Bridge, near Pevensey, Sussex, on Jan. 29th, 1907. Thinking it was a variety of the Skylark, he sent it to Mr Bristow, taxid-ermist, of St Leonards, and the latter received it by post on Jan. 31. It was brought to me for examination in the flesh, but, unfortunately, I was out, and I did not see it till the following day, when it was mounted and in the braces. It is an adult male in winter plumage. The female was brought to me in the flesh on Feb. 2, 1907, by Mr Bristow, who had just received it by post from Lydd, Kent, where it had been shot on Jan. 31st. It was accompanied by a male and two females, and the man who shot it aimed at the male bird as being a stranger to him, but the shot killed the female.

Since these two were obtained, I hear from my brother that another male was shot at Lydd, Kent, on Feb. 18th, and another at Rye, Sussex, on Feb. 16, and that others have been seen.

The weather during the previous week had been very cold.

On Jan. 23 there was an easterly gale, a most unusual thing at that time of year, and the following days were cold with north and north-east winds. The wind blew strongly from the south-east on the 28th, but was back again in the north and north-east on the 30th and 31st.

The first record of this bird in Western Europe seems to have been in Belgium, for M. Alphonse Dubois writes that in March 1850 his father found one (captured out of a flock) in the Brussels market; next, one was taken in 1852 near Antwerp; and again, in the same district, about a dozen were taken between 1880 and 1885, two of which are in a private collection. On Heligoland, as recorded by Gätke, a female was obtained on April 27th, 1874, and a male on July 27th, 1892. Near Grimmen, in Pomerania, as well as in Lower Austria, examples are said to have been taken.

This species inhabits the Steppes of Southern Russia, Transcaspia, and Western Siberia. Its occurrence so far west is comparable to the occurrence of *Melanocorypha sibirica* in Kent in Jan. 1902. I would suggest that this flock of Black Larks migrated in front of the wave of very cold weather, which spread westward over Europe in January, and that, after striking the Kent and Sussex coasts, they scattered, settling in suitable localities. It is quite possible we may hear of some having occurred elsewhere on our coasts or in other parts of Western Europe.

In congratulating Mr C.B. Ticehurst on the acquisition of these specimens, Mr Howard Saunders remarked that for some years he had been expecting the Black Lark as an addition to the list of wanderers to the British Islands. He proceeded to point out that after being treated somewhat vicariously as compared with districts to the north of Suffolk, the south-east and south of England had been closely watched of late years by observers such as Mr M.J. Nicoll, the Messrs Ticehurst, Mr W.R. Butterfield, and others. The result had been the discovery in that area of both forms of the Eared Wheatear, the White-spotted Bluethroat, Cetti's Warbler, the Nubian Shrike, the Snow-finch, Baird's Sandpiper, the Mediterranean Great Shearwater, etc.; while researches had shown that the occurrences of several species already on the list indicated a frequent tendency to 'overshoot' the ordinary limits on the vernal migration northward.

From the report on the Club's meeting on 17 June 1908.

Mr M.J. Nicoll exhibited an example of a Bunting new to the British Fauna, and made the following remarks:

I exhibit a male example of the South European Large-billed Reed-bunting, *Emberiza pyrrhuloides palustris* (Savi) [=*E. schoeniclus intermedia*]. This bird was shot on Romney Marsh in Kent between Rye and Lydd on the 26th of May, 1908, and was brought to Mr Bristow, of St Leonard's. I examined it directly after it had been mounted and while the feet were still soft. This is the first time that an example of this subspecies has been procured in the British Islands. The typical form, *E.p. pyrrhuloides* [also now treated as *E.s. intermedia*], Pall., has occurred on Heligoland.

Dr Sclater called attention to the rare birds from the shores of Kent and Sussex, which had been shown at the recent meeting of the South-eastern Union of Scientific Societies at Hastings. Mr G. Bristow (of St Leonard's) had exhibited forty-six excellently mounted specimens obtained in the district. Among these were examples of *Melanocorypha yeltoniensis* (a pair), *Lanius nubicus*, *Motacilla melanocephala*, *Saxicola occidentalis* [= *Oenanthe hispanica*], *Aegialitis vocifera* [= *Charadrius vociferus*], and *Totanus solitarius* [= *Tringa solitaria*], all of which had already been exhibited at previous meetings of the Club.

137

The Black Woodpecker in Britain

The following carefully argued case for the inclusion of the Black Wood-pecker *Dryocopus martius* in the British list is slightly abbreviated from R.S.R. Fitter's paper in the *Bulletin* of 1959, the main omission being the detailed county-by-county list of all the claimed occurrences printed as an appendix. In spite of this, the Black Woodpecker has not been admitted to the British list. It was considered for admission in 1960, soon after this paper appeared (*The Ibis* 102: 630), and again in 1980 (*The Ibis* 122: 568), and was rejected on both occasions.

During the first half of the nineteenth century the Great Black Woodpecker, *Dryocopus (Picus) martius* (Linnaeus), was an accepted member of the British avifauna, with the status of a rare vagrant. From Latham (1787) onwards no historian of our birds questioned its right to be considered British. Not until 1871 were any serious doubts expressed, but in that year J. H. Gurney's summary in the fifth volume of Dresser's *Birds of Europe* completely discredited its British status in the eyes not only of almost all contemporary ornithologists (J.E. Harting was a notable exception), but of most later ones as well.

Newton, in his revised edition of Yarrell, pronounced that Gurney had 'completely disposed of the claims set up in nearly every instance', and in his own *Dictionary of Birds* abandoned even this qualifying phrase and said that 'the persistency with which many writers on British birds have for years included this species among them is a marvellous instance of the durability of error, for not a case of its asserted occurrence in this country is on record that will bear investigation, and the origin of the mistake has been more than once shewn'. Nobody would guess from this sweeping judgement that Newton himself, at the age of 18, had published a record of the Great Black Woodpecker in Essex, which he seems never to have specifically withdrawn.

Yet all the time Gurney's great work of demolition of unsound records contained an unwitting error. For many years one of the few remaining old records of the Great Black Woodpecker which retained the confidence of ornithologists was Lord Stanley's of one said to have been shot in Lancashire. Indeed the bird was virtually retained on the British list only because it was not thought possible to doubt the word of so eminent a noble-man. Then it was discovered that in Stanley's copy of Latham he had erased the relevant passage and written in the margin 'a mistaken idea'. From this E. Newman (*Zool.* 23: 9626; 1865) jumped to the conclusion that an error in identification had been made, and that the bird in question must have been a Great Spotted Woodpecker (*Dendrocopos major*). This erroneous guess sealed the doom of the Great Black Woodpecker as a British bird. For, as demonstrated below in Appendix I (Lancashire 1) [the Appendices are not included here], Newman guessed the wrong kind of mistake. What Stanley meant was that the bird had been shot in Dorset, not Lancashire. His bird was in fact the Blandford specimen mentioned by Pulteney (1799). This discovery alone should serve to restore the Great Black Woodpecker to the British list.

Under the influence of Newton and without adequate consideration of subsequently accruing records, the Great Black Woodpecker was rejected by both BOU lists, in 1883 and 1915, and by Witherby and his collaborators in the successive *Handlist* (1912), *Practical Handbook* (1919–24) and *Handbook of British Birds* (1938–41). Yet by 1938 at least thirty records (not counting the East Anglian ones) had been published since Gurney's summary, some of the most convincing of them in Witherby's own journal *British Birds.* Not until the appearance of Volume 4 of David Bannerman's *The Birds of the British Isles* (1955) did an ornithologist of the front rank once more admit the Great Black Woodpecker to full treatment in a general work on British birds, and even Bannerman suspended judgement on the bird's claim to be British.

The aim of the present paper is to suggest that the treatment of the Great Black Woodpecker by ornithologists since Gurney and Newton is another marvellous instance of the durability of error, the error not of credulity but of unco incredulity. This is by no means to say that Gurney and Newton were wrong, in the light of the then existing knowledge, nor to deny that some erroneous claims have been made, but the fact that error and even fraud have occurred in the past is no reason either for ignoring new facts or for not taking a fresh look at old ones.

No bird not on the official British list has so often been recorded wild in Britain as the Great Black Woodpecker. I have collected no fewer than 82 records, a few here published for the first time, of which ten are rather vague general statements, 49 are specific sight records and at least 26 have at some time been backed by specimens, in one case a clutch of eggs. (These figures do not add up because a few records fall into two categories). Actual error or fraud has been proved in only four cases, though in a number of others the description of the bird is unsatisfactory in a material respect, the provenance of the specimen is suspect, or the birds are known to have been in captivity. There remain, however, nine general statements, 17 specimen records and 37 sight records, which there is no specific reason for rejecting, even though some of them still contain elements of doubt. Out of these 54 records seven have been selected as being unassailable in their claims, viz. three specimen records (listed as Dorset 1, Wiltshire 1 and Yorkshire 8 in Appendix 1) and four sight records (Hertfordshire 2, Brecon 2, Notts 2 and Cheshire 1). It is on these seven that the burden of the case for reconsidering the status of the Black Woodpecker as a British bird rests.

Before turning to a detailed analysis of the surviving uninvalidated records, we may examine the general arguments that have been advanced against the possibility of the Great Black Woodpecker being a British bird. First among these is the fact that, in common with most other Woodpeckers, it is normally sedentary. Some ornithologists have believed so strongly that Great Black Woodpeckers could not reach our shores unaided that they have committed such absurdities as suggesting (before they were known to be escapes) that the observers who saw the Great Black Woodpeckers in the Brandon district must actually have seen Nutcrackers (*Nucifraga*). However, even sedentary birds tend to wander slightly at the end of the breeding season, and the Great Black Woodpecker is in fact recorded as a scarce winter visitor to Denmark, where it does not breed (Bannerman, 1955). Furthermore, since 1913 the Great Black Woodpecker has started to breed in the Netherlands and is now widespread in the woods of the eastern and southern provinces (van Ijzendoorn, 1950). These must have come from somewhere, and if birds can wander into Holland and Denmark there is no reason why they should not occasionally be wind-drifted across the North Sea. In fact, however, the only British Great Black Woodpecker record suggesting a recent immigrant was Cornwall 1, where the bird might have been coming from the Pyrenees.

The next line of defence is that the birds recorded in Britain may have been wrongly identified. In one instance (Norfolk 1) the Great Spotted Woodpecker (*Dendrocopos major*) is known to have been misrecorded as Great Black, and Devon 3 & 4 and Scotland 2 may be due to the same error. Were it not for the proved example, one would have said that it was impossible to mistake anything else for so distinctive a bird as the Great Black Woodpecker, given a clear view at close range. A bird the size of a rook, coal black all over except for a red patch on the head, and having the conspicuously woodpecker-like habits of climbing trees and flying with marked undulations, could hardly be misidentified. Certainly nobody who had ever seen a Great Black Woodpecker in the field, or had heard its distinctive, far-carrying, loud, clear, fluty string of double call-notes, could fail to recognise it on meeting it again in England.

However, the crux of the sight-record question is that in the nineteenth century sight records were just not believed in, largely because very few of the leading ornithologists of the day had the skill or field experience to identify the rarer migrants or vagrants that might be met with. No bird was admitted to the British list until a dead British-taken specimen was produced. It was the Great Black Woodpecker's misfortune that despite the numerous specimens shot or alleged to have been shot in these islands, no indubitably British-taken skin had come down to posterity, as represented by Gurney and Newton, while none of the older ornithologists had at that time left any conclusive published evidence that he had himself seen a British-taken specimen. Sight records were quite unacceptable until one specimen had been authenticated, after which they might be grudgingly admitted in square brackets. This presumably explains Newton's curious later attitude to the Great Black Woodpecker sight record he himself reported in 1847 (Essex 1). Nowadays, such is the ill repute of many specimen records of the last hundred years, we have more confidence in a good field description by an experienced bird-watcher than in an old specimen in a museum. Unfortunately ornithologists of the last century just did not take field descriptions. It was the blind spot of a distinguished generation.

In 1871 Gurney was faced with a situation in which none of the specimens available could be authenticated as British-taken, the few old records by reliable ornithologists were distinctly vague, none of the numerous sight records had adequate field descriptions attached, and most had none. It would have been reasonable to suspend judgement at this point, but in fact the following generation of ornithologists, overawed by Gurney's massive research and Newton's emphatic pronouncements, seem to have made up their minds that the Great Black Woodpecker not only was not but could not be a British bird. Hence the curious neglect of every subsequent record, the scant attention paid to Clement Ley's convincing observations, the first with even partial field descriptions, and the open conspiracy that any post-1895 records should be attributed to the two ailing birds released in that year by Lord Lilford.

Another possibility, often suggested, is of confusion with melanic Green Woodpeckers (*Picus viridis*). Mr Bryan L. Sage, who is making a special study of heterochrosis in British birds, kindly informs me that he has never heard of a case of complete melanism in the Green Woodpecker, though he knows of one instance of partial melanism, an adult male with pale brown secondaries and wing coverts on the left wing, shot at Norwich in January 1886 (*Zoologist*, 1887, p. 416). (It is perhaps worth noting that there is no valid record of the Great Black Woodpecker for either Norfolk or Suffolk.) In the present study, only three records have come to light which sound at all like melanic Green Woodpeckers, viz. Surrey 4, Hertfordshire 1 and Berkshire 4. In each case the birds are clearly not normal Great Black Woodpeckers. Size alone, of course, should normally distinguish a Great Black from a melanic Green Woodpecker. It is clear, at any rate, that melanic Green Woodpeckers, if they exist, are much too scarce to account for more than a very small fraction of the 54 uninvalidated British records of the Great Black Woodpecker, many of which indeed are accompanied by descriptions and specimens which could not possibly be melanic Green Woodpeckers.

During the nineteenth and early twentieth centuries many collectors with more money that sense were prepared to offer high prices for British-taken rarities, and there is no doubt that at one time a number of Great Black Woodpeckers were in fact brought over with parcels of game from Scandinavia and passed off as British-taken. The two proved instances of this kind of fraud are Hampshire 2 and Berkshire 2, and the rumour included as Norfolk 2 probably comes into the same category. There is good reason to suppose that Yorkshire 6 & 7, both emanating from the Hull district in the same month (November) as Berkshire 2 and Norfolk 2 are also due to fraud. These five records all occurred between 1868 and 1879, from which period also dates Shropshire 1, a specimen whose provenance is unknown. The only other instance in which doubt has been successfully cast on the origin of a specimen is Devon 3, said to have been taken about 1830, but perhaps not in Devon; whether the doubt is due to fraud or honest muddle is not stated. There is no other evidence of commercial frauds as early as 1830.

Finally, it has often been suggested that any genuine Great Black Woodpeckers seen in Britain must have either escaped or been deliberately released from captivity. Woodpeckers of any kind, however, are rarely kept in captivity – they are not even mentioned by Goodwin (1956) – and according to Lord Lilford the bird he acquired for his collection in 1891 was 'the first Great Black Woodpecker that, so far as I know, has ever been seen in this country' (Lilford 1900). The only recorded escapes or introductions of Great Black Woodpeckers in the British Isles all took place in 1895 and 1897. Lilford released his two birds in 1895 because they were ailing in health, so it may be hazarded that they did not survive long. Then in 1897 seven or eight young birds were brought over from Sweden, presumably in late June or July, and kept for a time in an aviary near Brandon, Suffolk, before being released. Several were seen in various parts of the district during the next six years, but none more than 14 miles from Brandon, except for the birds reported in 1903 from Sheringham, 40 miles to the N.E. Finally, one bird escaped from the London Zoo on 9th October, 1897. Since the only positive evidence we have about the movements of introduced Great Black Woodpeckers shows that they did not move very far, it is sheer speculation to suppose that birds seen more than a hundred miles away in the years following 1897 must have come from Brandon. It is even wilder speculation to suppose that Great Black Woodpeckers seen in Britain at any other period must have come from some unrecorded source of introduction.

To facilitate analysis of the 82 records of the Great Black Woodpecker in Britain – there are none for Ireland – I have devised a system of four categories of reliability for the specimen records and eight categories for the sight records and general statements. The records themselves are listed in Appendix 1, together with the evidence on which they are based.

Specimen records

Category 1: Satisfactory records, where there is no doubt as to the identity or provenance of the specimen. Four specimens fall into this category: Dorset 1, which Gurney did not know had passed into Lord Stanley's collection, and three, viz. Wiltshire 1, Middlesex 1 and Yorkshire 8, which were not known to Gurney. Wiltshire 1 is as well authenticated as any nineteenth-century record can now well be. Middlesex 1 is vouched for by Fothergill (1807) at a time when there is no reason to suspect importation frauds, but as it is such a very old record and Fothergill does not tell us how it came into his possession after being taken at Chelsea, it is not included in the seven records on which the case for the Great Black Woodpecker mainly rests. Saunders suggested that the 1897 Yorkshire specimen was one of the two sickly birds released in Northamptonshire two years previously, but this seems extremely unlikely. The Great Black Woodpeckers released 150 miles away in Suffolk in 1897 are ruled out because they were birds of the year, and the Yorkshire bird must have been plainly an adult, or Saunders could hardly have suggested it might have been a bird released two years before. (Young birds differ in having a less strong bill, the black not so pure and the red on the crown of the male duller and not so largely developed.) In the Yorkshire bird, therefore, we have the best possible evidence, a specimen shot under unimpeachable circumstances and identified by the foremost ornithologist of the day.

Category 2: Record not now provable because specimen lacking. This is the largest category of specimens, where it is a question of whether or not we believe the older ornithologists who recorded them. It contains 15 records localised to a country, viz. Somerset 1, Dorset 2, Isle of Wight 1, Hampshire 1, 2 & 4, Surrey 1 & 2, Middlesex 2, Lincolnshire 1, Notts 1, Yorkshire 3 & 5 and Scotland 2; and two unlocalised records, Great Britain 1 & 2, which could in fact refer to some of the localised ones. It is very hard to say today whether one can trust the judgement of Montagu and Howarth over Surrey 1 and of Pulteney over Dorset 2, or the certificate of the anonymous person who obtained Macgillivray's two specimens (Notts 1).

Category 3: Specimens of doubtful provenance, viz. Devon 3, Norfolk 2, Shropshire 1 and Yorkshire 6 & 7.

Category 4: Proven errors, viz. Hampshire 3, Berkshire 2, Norfolk 1 and Lancashire 1.

Sight records

Category 1: Satisfactory field description. Four records, none of them known to Gurney, fall within this category, viz. Hertfordshire 2, Brecon 2, Notts 2 and Cheshire 1. Of these four, one (Brecon) by a very eminent field ornithologist, the late J. Walpole-Bond, together with the two specimen records mentioned above (Wiltshire 1, Yorkshire 8), the main case for the British status of the Great Black Woodpecker rests. All the other records listed in Categories 2–5 below and in Category 2 of specimen records can be treated as supporting data for the main seven. Most of them no doubt will be generally acceptable when the main records are validated.

Category 2: Description unsatisfactory only in a minor detail, which might well have been due to observational error. Three records, viz. Cornwall 1 (bill curved), Surrey 3 (red on head not seen) and Brecon 1 (tail forked).

Category 3: Description inadequate or lacking, but observer experienced. Eight records, viz. Devon 5, Hampshire 6, Middlesex 3, Herefordshire 1 & 4 & 5 & 6, Yorkshire 1. Five of these are due to the Rev. Clement Ley, who was familiar with the Great Black Woodpecker abroad and more than once saw it at close range or heard its unmistakable call-note in Herefordshire and Devon.

Category 4: Description satisfactory apart from size. Three records, viz. Kent 1, Berkshire 3, Derbyshire 1. These are not included in Cat. 2 because size, though easy to misjudge, is so important a factor in identifying the Great Black Woodpecker, which is rook-size, not jackdaw-size as these three records suggest. The Green Woodpecker, however, *is* the size of a Jackdaw, so that the unrecorded melanic Green Woodpecker must be considered a possibility here.

Category 5: Description inadequate or lacking and record not now provable. This is the largest category of sight records, as the corresponding Cat. 2 was of specimen records. It contains 18 occurrences, viz. Somerset 2 & 3 & 4, Hampshire 1 & 2 & 5 & 7, Essex 1, Berkshire 1, Bucks 1, Gloucestershire 1, Herefordshire 2 & 3 & 8, Warwickshire 1, Rutland 1, Flintshire 1 and York-shire 2 & 9. Many of these records would have been accepted automatically if the Great Black Woodpecker had been an established member of the British avifauna ever since Latham's day, for there is no positive reason for doubting the identification of any of them.

Category 6: Description unsatisfactory in a material respect. Five records, viz. Surrey 2 & 4, Hertfordshire 1, Berkshire 4, Herefordshire 7. The middle three of these are the most likely melanic Green Woodpecker suspects.

Category 7: Obvious or proven error: none.

Category 8: Known and suspected escapes. Three known escapes, viz. Middlesex 4, Suffolk 1 and Northants 1. Suffolk 2–5 almost certainly and Norfolk 3 most probably stemmed from the Suffolk 1 introduction.

General Statements

Category 5: Description lacking and statement not now provable. Nine state-ments, viz. Devon 1 & 3 & 4, Dorset 3 & 4, Sussex 1, Northants 1, Worcester-shire 1 & 2. Little reliance can be placed on any of these mostly rather vague statements, some of which may in fact be due to confusion with the Great Spotted Woodpecker.

Category 7: Obvious or proven error. Scotland 1 is an ancient semantic error.

Breeding Records

A special word should perhaps be said about the two alleged breeding records of the Great Black Woodpecker in England. Surrey 2 is frankly incredible, owing to the extraordinary statement that the nest was in a hole in a wall, which was plastered up by the birds. This is not a habit of the Great Black nor of any of our three native Woodpeckers, while the Wryneck, which might nest in a wall, also does not plaster. Imagination boggles at the idea of anybody mistaking even a melanic Nuthatch for a Great Black Woodpecker! Hampshire 2 produced a clutch of eggs, but the experts who saw them could not agree on their identification, while the man who took them was a dealer and so is suspect*. It is possible that he found an abnormal Green Woodpecker clutch and tried to cash in by inventing a Great Black Woodpecker story, but there are no solid grounds for attempting to blacken his posthumous reputation in this way.

Geographical Distribution

When the uninvalidated records are mapped, a number of curious points emerge. Table I shows their distribution by Watsonian provinces.

The most noticeable thing is that, except for a single record for Shetland, there are no valid Great Black Woodpecker records north of Yorkshire, and only three (Cheshire 1, Flintshire 1, Shropshire 1) in the whole of north-west England and North and West Wales, down to Pembroke, Carmarthen, Radnor, Montgomery, Salop and Stafford. The east coast of England, where one would expect to find birds drifted across the North Sea, is, except for Yorkshire, singularly devoid of Great Black Woodpecker records. Indeed in the coastal counties from the Humber to Selsey Bill there are only four records (Lincolnshire 1, Essex 1, Kent 1 and Sussex 1), two of which are very vague, and none at all in Norfolk or Suffolk.

The pattern of Great Black Woodpecker records, indeed, does not suggest even irregular migration, but the presence in certain favoured areas of long-lived birds that have penetrated often well inland, after being drifted, either across the North Sea from Denmark to Yorkshire or across the Channel from the Pyrenees to the south coast of England. It is in fact the kind of pattern that might be expected in a normally sedentary species, whose occasional wanderings may be presumed to be in search of new territory. There are three of these favoured areas, the Home Counties, the New Forest and the southern Welsh Border country. The three Somerset records in the ten years 1935–44 are also interesting.

---

*He also claimed Little Owl (*Athene noctua*) breeding in the New Forest.

Table 1. Black Woodpecker records by Watsonian provinces

Watsonian Province	Total	Specimen Records	Sight Records	General Statements
Peninsula	9	1 Cat. 2	1 Cat. 2	3 Cat. 5
			1 Cat. 3	
			3 Cat. 5	
Channel	14	1 Cat. 1	2 Cat. 3	3 Cat. 5
		6 Cat. 2	3 Cat. 5	
Thames	11	1 Cat. 1	1 Cat. 1	
		3 Cat. 2	1 Cat. 2	
			1 Cat. 3	
			2 Cat. 4	
			2 Cat. 5	
Anglia				1 Cat. 5
Severn	12	1 Cat. 3	4 Cat. 3	2 Cat. 5
			5 Cat. 5	
S. Wales	2		1 Cat. 1	
			1 Cat. 2	
N. Wales	1		1 Cat. 5	
Trent	5	2 Cat. 2	1 Cat. 1	
			1 Cat. 4	
			1 Cat. 5	
Mersey	1		1 Cat. 1	
Humber	7	1 Cat. 1	1 Cat. 3	
		3 Cat. 2	2 Cat. 5	
Tyne	0			
Lakes	0			
Scotland	1	1 Cat. 2		

In the Home Counties there is a remarkable clumping of records in 1844–50, when Berkshire 1 (April 1844), Middlesex 3 (May 1845), Essex 1 (June 1847) and Surrey 2 (1848–50) could all have been caused by a couple of birds wandering about the Home Counties, ending with a foray into the Midlands to produce Rutland 1 (c.1850) and Warwickshire 1 (1851) within about 25 miles of each other.

In or near the New Forest there are scattered records over a period of about 75 years, in 1836–41, June 1862, c. 1887, May 1889 and June 1913, while the Dorset and Isle of Wight records and Hampshire 4 are all within 25 to 30 miles of the New Forest and two of them within the same period.

The most suggestive aggregation of records is in the Welsh border area of

Herefordshire, Forest of Dean and Brecon, where the following series of nine or ten occurrences is on record:

Ruckhall Wood, Eaton Bishop, June c. 1874
Belmont, 1 mile from Eaton Bishop, spring 1879
Weston under Penyard, summer 1880
Dinas, near Brecon, May 1885
Pengethley Gorse, Ross-on-Wye, twice prior to 1888
Fownhope, prior to 1888
(Little Doward, prior to 1888)
Forest of Dean, 1890s
Kington, November 1901
Builth Wells, April 1903

These birds were reported by seven different observers, none of them apparently in touch with each other, and it is hard to resist the conclusion that one or two Great Black Woodpeckers, perhaps occasionally breeding, were present in that comparatively little-watched area for a period of thirty years. It is at any rate much more likely that the crucial Builth Wells record of 1903 [a bird very well observed by J. Walpole-Bond] was a survivor from this small population than that it had originated from the Suffolk introduction nearly 140 miles to the eastward six years previously.

* * *

In the 34 years since this paper was written there have been no further reports of Black Woodpeckers in Britain (R. Fitter, *Birding World* 2 (1992): 75–7), in spite of the vastly increased number of general birdwatchers and rarity hunters; so it seems that, whatever their origin, the scattered population that undoubtedly existed up to the 1940s has died out. However, it is not unlikely that the Black Woodpecker will appear again and perhaps establish itself, as it has been spreading into the lowlands of northwestern Europe in recent decades, with the maturation of conifer plantations, and now nests close to the North Sea and English Channel coast (*Birds of the Western Palearctic*, vol. 4).

Assisted passage

Until the mid-1950s the idea of assisted passage was not generally accepted and most records of North American landbirds in particular were dismissed as being of captive origin. The BOURC's first report (in the *Ibis* in 1956) after the 1952 *Check-list of the Birds of Great Britain and Ireland* concluded that 'the possibility of so-called "assisted passage" should not necessarily deny to a bird the right of admittance to the British list'. Since then, 17 species of parulid warbler have been added to the list, along with a number of other North American landbirds. Yellow Warbler *Dendroica petechia* was admitted to the list in 1971 on the basis of a 1964 record. The Durham specimen has not been accepted. The Green-backed Heron *Butorides striatus* noted by Meinertzhagen was accepted in 1974 as the first British record.

A.G. KNOX

From the report on the Club's meeting on 15 February 1905.

Mr E. Bidwell, through the kindness of Mr Herbert W. Grace, of Hallgarth, Winlaton-on-Tyne, was enabled to exhibit a specimen of the Yellow Warbler [*Dendroeca aestiva* (Gmel.)] obtained in Great Britain. Mr Grace had furnished the following particulars:

This bird was picked up on the Newcastle and Shotley Bridge Road, near Axwell Park, in the county of Durham, in the second or third week of May 1904. It was taken by the lad who found it to Mr John Walker, a bird-stuffer at Bladon, who set it up and sold it to my game-watcher's son, from whom I bought it. I have my information from Mr Walker. The bird was quite fresh when he bought it, and had a broken leg, supposed to have been caused by flying against a telegraph-wire.

The Yellow Warbler is distributed throughout North America, except in the south-western part, and breeds throughout nearly the whole of its North-American range. It goes south in winter to Central America and northern South America.

A discussion followed in which several members took part.

Mr Rothschild thought it quite possible, taking into consideration its migratory habits, that the bird might have received an 'assisted passage', but Mr Howard Saunders was of the opinion that it had probably escaped from a cage. Mr Seth-Smith said that, as far as he was aware, no species of *Dendroeca* had ever been brought to this country in captivity, but Dr Hartert observed that in Curaçao a closely allied species, *D. rufopileata*, was frequently kept as a cage-bird. Finally, Dr Sclater said that he saw no reason why the bird should not reach England as an accidental autumn visitor, and he pointed out that the distance between northern South America and the northern parts of North America was not greater than the distance between South America and England, and that birds blown out of their course might easily reach our shores.

Dr Hartert took the opportunity of calling attention to the example of the Sprosser Nightingale (*Daulias philomela*) [= Thrush Nightingale *Luscinia luscinia*] exhibited at a recent meeting of the Club [*cf. Bull BOC* xv, no. cx, p. 20 (1904)]. Though this specimen showed no traces of having been kept in captivity, he had no doubt that it had escaped from a cage, for all the Sprosser Nightingales had left NE Germany two months previous to the date (22nd October) when the specimen had been procured in Kent. Large numbers of this bird were annually captured and exported by dealers, and if well cared for would show little or no trace of having been kept for a month or two in captivity.

From the report on the Club's meeting on 19 April 1955.

Colonel R. Meinertzhagen made the following remarks:

Long-distance assisted sea passages by birds

During the past few years an ever-increasing number of American birds have been recorded in Britain. This is primarily due to a larger number of watchers and their increased competence in identification. The popular theory of 'drift' due to predominant westerly winds, though it may account for the initial stage of the trip across the Atlantic, does not take into consideration long-distance assisted sea passages taken advantage of by many birds. It is my experience that almost all birds when out of sight of land will fly towards and usually rest on a ship, often remaining the night and sometimes long periods.

I give a few cases of long-distance assisted passages.

1. Four House Crows (*Corvus splendens*) came aboard a ship off Colombo and remained for six days, crossing the Indian Ocean, only leaving the ship when Somaliland was sighted (Davis, *Auk*, 1951: 529).

2. A Wagtail (*Motacilla alba*) was carried the whole length of the Red Sea from Perim to Suez, feeding on insects on board (Davis, *Auk*, 1951: 529).

3. A Yellow Wagtail (*Motacilla flava*) came aboard a ship off Egypt and was seen daily for ten days, finally leaving when only 900 miles from Boston. It fed on flies near some cages full of monkeys (Phillips, *Ibis*, 1952: 530).

4. In October, 1929, twelve brown thrush-like birds flew aboard a ship off Newfoundland and only left the ship when in sight of Ireland (Tait, *Country Life*, 8th Apr., 1954).

5. European starlings left a ship when off the coast of Venezuela (Meiklejohn, *The Times*, 1st Dec., 1954).

6. A Hoopoe (*Upupa epops*) travelled on a ship from Aden to Suez (Davis, *Auk*, 1951: 529).

7. Three Nightjars (*Caprimulgus europaeus*) came aboard a ship at Suez in January and remained on board the whole length of the Red Sea, leaving near Perim. (*Personal observation*).

8. In 1895 we received a Snowy Owl (*Nyctea*) alive which had come aboard a ship off Nova Scotia in October and was caught when in sight of Ireland. It lived in our aviaries until 1900. (*Personal observation*).

9. A Greenland Falcon (*Falco rusticolus*) came aboard a ship off Nova Scotia in 1921 and remained on the ship until the Scillies were sighted when it flew off, and, presumably the same bird, remained at Tresco the whole winter. (*Personal communication from Miss Dorrien Smith who was on the ship and Major Dorrien Smith of Tresco*).

10. The American race of the Peregrine (*Falco peregrinus anatum*) flew aboard a ship off Newfoundland and remained on board for three days, a passage of over 1,000 miles, when it was caught and killed. I have the specimen in my collection.

11. A Little Green Heron (*Butorides striatus virescens*) came aboard a ship off the Bahamas and remained until in sight of the Azores when it was caught and killed. The specimen is in my collection.

A specimen of this Heron was shot at Penrose in Cornwall in October, 1889, and should be accepted as a valid British record. I have spoken to the keeper who shot it and have seen the stuffed specimen.

12. At 9 a.m. on October 10th, a tired Robin (*Erithacus*) came aboard a ship 200 miles south of Ushant, accepting food on board and only leaving the ship on reaching London Docks on October 12th. This type of assisted passage might well account for Mediterranean birds occurring in Britain. This Robin travelled 400 miles in reversed migrational direction (*Bird Notes*, xxvi, 4, 1955, p. 105).

Colonel Meinertzhagen asked what view the Records Sub-Committee of the BOU was going to take in view of these instances of assisted passages.

Mr Max Nicholson said he thought the only criterion available was whether the bird had come as a captive or voluntarily, but Mr James Robertson Justice said that if this was to be, there was obviously no limit. For instance he knew an American in California, who had tamed Humming Birds to sit on his finger. If he should come to Britain together with a Humming Bird perched on his finger, would this constitute a new British record! He also referred to a Whimbrel (*Numenius phaeopus*) which he had carried to South America on board one of HM ships in the War.

Professor Meiklejohn mentioned an instance of a wild falcon being fed on board one of Frederick II's ships in the thirteenth century and in his talk later showed a slide of the illustration of this.

Introductions

Introductions of non-native species anywhere in the world have rarely proved desirable. These particular proposals would have been equally inappropriate. The Rock Bunting *Emberiza cia* has now occurred six times, and the Blue Rock Thrush *Monticola solitarius* is currently under consideration for admission to the British list.

A.G. KNOX

From the report on the Club's meeting on 12 June 1918.

Mr H.M. Wallis brought forward the following proposal for a limited and carefully guarded scheme of acclimatisation:

During the last century the list of British birds has been steadily growing. Systematic watching at Spurn, Cley, certain coast islands, and Romney Marsh have brought the assurance that there are possibly fifty species of birds which occasionally touch us on migration, and a dozen or more which habitually do so in certain weathers. This is interesting, but affords small comfort to the bulk of working ornithologists, who cannot afford to put in a week on the Norfolk coast on the chance of spotting a Barred Warbler, a Blue-throat, or Shore Lark.

We are willing to take the words of the fortunate observers who get down to Dungeness for a weekend and return with accounts of Surf-scoter and Cream-coloured Courser. When we get there these birds are sure to have moved on. We should prefer that they stayed. For the list of British birds is wholly increased by visitors. Our residents get few, or no additions, saving the doubtfully welcome Little Owl. Indeed they tend to diminish.

My proposal amounts to this, that the BOC should appoint a committee to consider the feasibility of introducing a few birds to these islands as permanent resident, breeding species.

I am not ambitious. The introduction of a new migrant would be a very difficult business. If it were a European species its introduced members would in all likelihood attach themselves to their relatives in their winter quarters, and come no farther north than the main body of the clan. If we attempted to introduce North American migratory species, the geographical conditions would probably defeat us. The Channel, the Alps, the Mediterranean, and the Atlas and Sahara, oppose such formidable barriers to the inexperienced migrant that we might expect to fail.

I merely suggest that we make a beginning with certain selected resident forms whose known habits afford us no expectation that they would prove nuisances if our scheme succeeded.

The Blue Rock Thrush is an insect-eating bird. I am not aware that it attacks fruit. It has a graceful appearance, a charming colour, lively habits, and a sweet little song. It frequents houses, churches, and ruins. I suggest that it might be introduced into the Cheddar Gorge as an experiment and carefully watched.

The Meadow Bunting (*E. cia*) breeds as near to us as Brest. It is a prettily marked creature, does no harm, and is so rare as a visitor that nobody ever expects to see it along our shores. Try it on the Chilterns.

The Alpine Chough has never occurred with us, for the Oxfordshire occurrence was an escape. This bird is not a coast-dweller, and if introduced into Scotland, Derbyshire, and the Lakes, might settle with us, for it apparently does not move far from its stations. Its wild note, its aerial gymnastics, and cheery habits endear it to those who have made its acquaintance in Switzerland, the Tyrol, and the Pyrenees. It has no known vices, and would get along wherever coleoptera and snails could be found.

I would like to suggest, in conclusion, that selections should be made among birds from the temperate zones which have never occurred in Europe; say from Japan, Vancouver, etc., and attempts made to introduce them here, giving preference to quiet coloration and good voice, rather than to brilliant plumage which would attract the Sunday gunner. Our working class is still too uneducated to assist experiments which call for self-restraint, as the North Repps attempts with Parrots showed.

The Chairman [Lord Rothschild] said that he entirely disapproved of all acclimatisation. He considered it undesirable for several reasons. From the point of view of the systematic worker it was deplorable, for often when extraneous specimens were introduced they bred with the native races and destroyed their local characteristics, while often introduced species, through finding specially congenial conditions, increased in vast numbers and become a destructive pest.

In the case of such birds as the Pheasant and Red-legged Partridge, introduced for sport, the danger was not so great, as they were kept under control under more or less artificial conditions.

Conservation

Protection of the Red Kite

Members of the BOC took the initiative, both practically and financially, in protecting the Red Kite in Wales, and from the beginning their efforts were reported at some length in the *Bulletin*. The following extracts speak for themselves. How much has changed since those early days of conservation – but how unchanged are the threats – is well summarised by Roger Lovegrove, RSPB representative in Wales, whose comments (pp. 163–4) bring the story up to date.

From the report on the Club's meeting on 18 February 1903.

Mr E. Hartert read to the meeting a letter from the Rev. Francis C.R. Jourdain, enclosing another letter from Dr J.H. Salter. It was agreed that both of these letters should be published in full in the *Bulletin*.

At a meeting of the BOC held on May 31, 1900, a resolution was carried 'That any member of the BOU directly or indirectly responsible for the destruction of nest, eggs, young, or parent birds of ... Kite ... should be visited with the severest censure of the Union.'

It is perhaps somewhat unfortunate that though this resolution was unanimously carried at a meeting of the BOC, no steps appear to have been taken to confirm it at any of the annual meetings of the BOU. This is the more to be regretted as the resolution, as it stands, is somewhat imperfectly drawn up.... But what I wish more particularly to point out is that as a protective measure in the case of the Kite the resolution appears to have had no effect. The following notes are from the pen of Dr J.H. Salter, and it will be seen that there exists even now a market for every nest that can be taken at £5 apiece. Who is responsible for this state of things? For ten years past at least this nest-harrying business has been systematically carried on; yet there is no

153

cessation in the demand. Does it arise from wealthy collectors who are not members of the Union? If so, the resolution becomes a mere 'self-denying ordinance' and is of no practical value. When it is remembered that every pair is regularly robbed twice a year it is evident that there is a large body of collectors who are indifferent to the action of the BOC, or else that the extermination of the species is sought as a speculation to enhance the value of the eggs already acquired. Nest-watching in this district is attended with peculiar difficulties, as will be seen from Dr Salter's notes, but something may yet be done if the landowners can be convinced of the importance of preserving this splendid bird. For this reason Mr Hartert has kindly consented to bring the matter before the BOC as it is proposed to take steps before the nesting season commences, and the annual meeting of the BOU falls too late in the year for the purpose.

Clifton Village Francis C.R. Jourdain
Ashburne, Derbyshire
Feb. 16, 1903

I take the present opportunity of enlisting the sympathies of members of the B.O. Club on behalf of the few remaining Welsh Kites. For all practical purposes the Kite now breeds nowhere in the British Islands but in a very limited district of South Wales. It is difficult to speak with certainty as to the exact number which remain, but there are certainly three, and probably five or six pairs – eight would be the outside limit. Taking the British Islands as a whole, the Kite is thus one of our rarest resident Raptores. Though thus reduced, its numbers do not appear to have decreased much during the past ten years. Most of the large landowners protect it so far as they are able; the farmers and shepherds are apathetic or indifferent. Its haunts are not threatened by the spread of cultivation, and they lie beyond the pale of game-preserving. Hence it is only very occasionally that a Kite is shot, and, if only allowed to breed, the race might still have a long lease of life. It is, however, most exceptional for any of these pairs to bring off young, owing to the greed of the egg-collectors.

The Kite resorts year after year to the same oak-wood, and there builds or repairs its large and conspicuous nest before there is a leaf upon the trees. These localities are well known, and the nests are invariably raided. Private collectors might in time be satisfied, but not so the dealers – some of them so-called 'naturalists.' One of these, hailing from Pembrokeshire, has visited the district annually for the past ten years, and has seldom failed to secure the contents of three nests. He states that at £5 the clutch he has far more orders for Kites' eggs than he can supply. No young are reared to take the place of an occasional bird which is shot, and thus the species dwindles and must, but for timely action, soon become extinct in Wales. Its extermination will be due solely to the egg-collectors, few of whom have any interest in the bird itself or know anything of its haunts. To all appearances there must be wealthy private collectors who wish to acquire a large series of the eggs of this vanishing species, probably with the idea of their value being much enhanced when the bird itself has finally vanished. Some ten years since the thanks of the Zoological Society of London were conveyed to a number of naturalists in mid-Wales for their efforts to protect the Kite. Several farmers and shepherds also do their best, in spite of the large bribes which are offered. But such attempts at protection are very rarely successful. The egg-stealers watch their chance, come at earliest daylight or (as in a recent instance) while the farmer is at church. It is hoped that the BOC will issue an appeal, asking naturalists to refrain from buying British-taken eggs of the Kite. If the members would also give strong expression to their opinions as to the desirability of trying to retain this fine species as a British bird, such an appeal (backed by the names of prominent naturalists) could be forwarded to Welsh landowners and would be likely to stimulate their interest in the Kite and increase their desire to protect it. Two county councils (out of three concerned) have taken out orders protecting both the bird and its eggs, but, in the absence of all provision for its enforcement, such legislation remains of course a dead letter.

As we fail to influence public opinion and thus decrease the demand for the Kites' eggs, nothing remains but to employ watchers. Arrangements are being made to try this plan during the coming breeding season. In the event of its being successful an appeal will probably be made another year to well-wishers of the Kite asking them to aid in defraying the expense, which will be considerable. But as this mode of protection is first to be tried tentatively in one or two cases, it is unnecessary to ask for such assistance at present.

University College of Wales   J.H. Salter
Aberystwith
Feb. 13, 1903

A discussion followed, in which Mr Rothschild, Mr Howard Saunders, Mr Hartert, and others took part, and it was then unanimously resolved:

1. That the thanks of the Club be given to Mr Jourdain and Dr Salter for calling the attention of the Members to the threatened extinction of the Kite in Great Britain.
2. That a 'Kite' Committee be appointed, to consist of Mr J.L. Bonhote, Mr W.E. de Winton, Mr E.G.B. Meade-Waldo, the Hon. Walter Rothschild, MP, Mr Howard Saunders, and Mr Watkin Watkins, to take steps to procure the preservation of the Kite, and that a fund be raised to prevent the molestation of the birds during the nesting season, and to procure the conviction of anyone found robbing the nests or offering money for the eggs.
3. That Mr E. Cambridge Phillips be asked to join with Dr Salter in endeavouring to secure protection for the Kites, and in the administration of any

funds that the Committee may deem advisable to depute to them for that purpose.

The sum of £47 was subscribed in the room by the Members present, for the above-mentioned fund, and £7 in addition towards the fund for rewarding anyone obtaining a conviction. Further subscriptions are solicited.

From the report on the Club's meeting on 28 June 1905.

Mr Meade-Waldo, treasurer of the 'Kite Fund,' stated that when he took over the secretaryship from Mr Witherby, early this spring, he at once wrote to Dr Salter. The latter replied that he considered the subject had been so well ventilated during the last two years that the chances of success were greater than they had been before, provided the watchers were *sufficiently well paid*. So far as he could ascertain, there were three pairs of Kites and one or two odd birds. Later, he wrote to say that there were three nests, but that one had been robbed. On June 21st he wrote that two nests had been well watched night and day, and that each contained two young nearly ready to fly. Mr Meade-Waldo stated that if these young were allowed to leave the nest in safety the rewards to be paid to the watchers would exhaust all the fund already paid up; but the appeal had been so liberally responded to in the first instance that all the money promised had not been claimed, and he felt sure that when an appeal was again made it would be equally well supported.

The Club passed an unanimous vote of thanks to Dr Salter for the trouble he had taken.

From the report on the Club's meeting on 26 May 1909.

The Rev. D. Edmondes Owen and Mr A. Gwynne Vaughan, who had been specially invited to attend the meeting as guests of the Club, gave an account of the efforts which are being made to protect the Kite (*Milvus ictinus*) in Wales.

The Rev. D. Edmondes Owen commenced by giving an interesting sketch of the life-history of certain animals, which, although once common in Wales, had now either vanished or were rapidly disappearing. Of these the bear, wolf, wild cattle, marten, and wild cat were mentioned, while the badger was reported to be still exceptionally numerous in the counties of Brecon and Radnor.

The Buzzard (*Buteo vulgaris*) now only merited the name of 'common' in mid-Wales. In a parallelogram with Glandovey, Knighton, Brecon, and Lampeter as its four corners there were no less than 60 or 70 pairs of this magnificent bird. A few years ago it was fast disappearing, but at the present time it was holding its own, thanks to the interest now taken in the rarer Welsh birds as a direct outcome of the Kite-protection movement.

The Raven (*Corvus corax*) was also very common in the same locality, and would no doubt continue to thrive there long after it had disappeared from less favoured counties.

Mr Owen then made the following remarks:

The question that naturally suggests itself is, what makes mid-Wales the home of these vanishing species? One would naturally expect them to choose the high and rugged mountains of Carnarvon and Merioneth. But when we realise that sheep and ponies depasture the hills of mid-Wales all the year round, whereas they are brought to the lowlands from the high and bare mountains of the north during the winter months, no further comment is necessary. Even in a mild winter there would be sufficient carrion on these hills to sustain life, while in a winter of great severity, when the needs of these birds would be greater, the supply of carrion would be much more plentiful.

This, undoubtedly, is one of the chief reasons why the Kite (*Milvus ictinus*) has survived in our neighbourhood after becoming extinct in other parts.

Sixty years ago the Kite was fairly common all over Wales, but particularly so in the district we have named. There are farmers still living who remember as many as 30 Kites which roosted regularly in one huge tree; and most of the old crofters on the hills of Radnorshire, Breconshire, and even of Cardiganshire will tell you that one of their boyish cares in the spring of the year was to guard the broods of chickens from the depredations of the Kite, which was then as common as the Carrion-crow (*Corvus corone*) is now.

Between the years 1850 and 1880 the range of the Kite became greatly reduced. Twenty-seven years ago one was shot near Craven Arms (Salop) and was regarded as a rare bird. This specimen is now in the possession of the vicar of Disserth, Radnorshire. About the same time several were shot near Symond's Yat and were considered rare.

With the advent of the breech-loading gun and the stricter preservation of the Grouse, the Kite suffered further persecution. To quote an example: on a grouse-moor in Radnorshire one keeper, who is still living, shot 30 Kites; he often followed them to their nesting-haunts and frequently destroyed both old birds.

A graphic description was given us the other day of how he killed the last pair which had attempted to breed in the Edw Valley. The birds, which were evidently old and wily, would not come within range, so he got the farmers to assist him in building a large bower near the nest, and from this shelter he soon secured both birds.

The Kite continued to breed in the Wye Valley, seven miles from these grouse-moors, until about eight years ago, when, to our certain knowledge, two young Kites were shot, and probably the old pair also.

Guns and traps were doubtless the chief cause of the earlier decrease of the Kite. They made the bird rare enough for its skin and eggs to become much coveted prizes for the collector.

The first collector appeared on the scene some twenty years ago, and he continued to loot systematically and successfully until a prominent member of the British Ornithologists' Club used his influence and compelled him to abandon his annual visits to the district.

During the greater part of this period the Kites suffered cruelly. The old birds were ruthlessly shot and trapped by keepers and farmers and no young appeared to fill the gaps. It was patent that if some drastic steps were not taken *Milvus ictinus* would soon be a mere memory.

Fortunately Dr Salter, who had for some years done all in his power to protect the Kite, reported the state of affairs to Mr Meade-Waldo, who promptly took practical steps to prevent the final disappearance of one of our finest Raptores.

Dr Salter was so tied by his professorial duties during term time that he could not visit the various breeding-haunts, and hearing of a man who was devoting all his time to studying the habits of our rare birds he requested him to assist in the protection of the Kite. How the Kites fared that year is known to several members of the Club. Five years ago a book was published which gave away the localities, and since that time egg-looters from all parts of the country have been visiting the district in every-increasing numbers, making the work of the protector extremely difficult. It is clear that without the help accorded to Dr Salter and ourselves by Mr Meade-Waldo and other members of this Club the Kite would, ere this, have been exterminated; even now it is doing little more than maintaining its ground.

Five years ago there were, to the best of our knowledge, only three pairs and an odd bird left. Today we have five pairs for certain and possibly one or two other couples. Last year, so far as the protected nests were concerned, the result was nil, but it was satisfactory to know that the old birds were not destroyed.

This is a point gained, because, even since the rigid protection was established, two old birds were shot near their nests. The more we protect the more our difficulties seem to multiply. The Carrion-crow, unsuspected before, destroyed two nests last year. This, however, is a vanishing danger, because, thanks to the action of Lord Cawdor, at least 80 Carrion-crows have been killed within the last six months.

It is feared that some of the Kites that now survive are too old for breeding. Dr Salter had a suspicion that this was the case some years ago and on one occasion went so far as to say that the birds were doomed for that reason.

Last year the eggs in one nest were infertile, and we are sorry to say that we have reason to believe that there are indications of this being the case in at least one nest this year.

158

The reports of our successes and failure in former years have reached you through Mr Meade-Waldo, to whose sympathy and support we owe so much.

Mr A. Gwynne Vaughan then read the following report:

Our tale this year is a tale of woe. The season commenced well. In Mrs Campbell-Davys's wood a pair built and lined their nest and in all probability laid eggs. This is one of the localities given away in the book we have mentioned. A great number of looters appeared on the scene about the middle of April, with the result that the nest was deserted; probably it was robbed. The pair may have built elsewhere, but we have been unable to locate them.

On Lord Cawdor's estate, where, as already reported, Kites have successfully nested for several years, a pair began to build this year in March and incubation commenced on the 6th April. On Thursday the 20th of May there were eggs but no young in the nest. The birds were not disturbed in any way; even the watchers did not go up to the nest between the 6th of April and the 20th of May. The eggs were evidently infertile. This pair of birds are possibly the same as those which nested in the same locality last year with a similar result.

In the same locality a third pair began building on the 20th of March. The first egg was laid on the 7th of April and the birds began to sit on the 10th. On the 2nd of May two young ones were hatched. On the 9th of May one of the young birds was found dead at the foot of the tree. No reason could be assigned for this. The weather was mild and calm.

So far the surviving bird is doing well.

A fourth nest was built in the early part of April on another estate. Three eggs were laid and on Tuesday the 20th of April, at the request of Lord Cawdor, four keepers were instructed to watch the nest. A hut was built 200 yards from the tree. On Saturday, the 24th of April, at 6 o'clock in the morning, one watchman relieved the other. At 6.30 the bird left the nest and hovered round the spot pestered by a great number of Rooks which built in the same wood. The Kite settled on a neighbouring tree, but did not return to the nest. She remained in the vicinity until the afternoon, when the male bird appeared: both then soared to a considerable height and flew right away.

These facts were reported to the owner of the estate, who promptly sent one of his keepers to fetch the eggs, and placed them in an incubator, but it is feared that nothing will result.

The night of the 23rd was wet and stormy, and, the nest being in a very exposed place, it seems probable that the bird got thoroughly soaked. We believe this to have been the cause of her deserting her domicile.

Since then the same pair have built another nest some miles nearer to the haunts which we have mentioned above.

A fifth pair of birds have been seen from time to time near Llwynmadoc, but we have not been able to locate the nest.

In the early part of the season a pair were seen on the Brecon Hills, but though we have made enquiries we have received no definite information.

This is but a sorry report. It is satisfactory only from one point: egg-looters have only succeeded in robbing one of the four nests.

We rejoice to say that the vast majority of landed proprietors and farmers are now keenly interested in and in full sympathy with the Kite-protection movement. This we attribute almost entirely to the very generous and tactful action taken by Lord Cawdor in the matter. Not only has he paid all the night-watchers, but both he and one of his sons as well as his agent, Mr Drummond, have visited the locality and have convinced the whole neighbourhood that it is a privilege and a duty to protect this rare and beautiful species.

On the motion of Mr Ogilvie-Grant it was unanimously decided that a letter should be sent from the Members of the Club to Lord Cawdor, to express their great appreciation of the active part which he had taken in the preservation of the Kites in Wales.

From the report on the Club's meeting on 16 March 1910.

Mr E.G.B. Meade-Waldo made a statement regarding the financial position of the Kite Fund for the years 1905–1909, and showed that the expenditure during that period had considerably exceeded the funds received. He said that it would shortly be necessary for him to appeal to the Members of the Club for further assistance. The records for the years 1905–1909 were on the whole extremely satisfactory, as was shown by the following statistics.

In 1905 the total number of Kites surviving in Wales was believed to be five. Of these, two pairs nested, and both succeeded in rearing two young birds. Total increase four.

In 1906 one nest contained three eggs, all of which hatched, and the young were successfully reared. The nest of the other pair was not found. Total increase three.

In 1907 one pair reared two young birds, and a second pair was observed in quite a different locality accompanied by two young birds. Two other nests were known to have been destroyed. Total increase four.

In 1908 six nests were known. In two of these the eggs were 'clear', in two the young, when a few days old, were killed by Carrion-crows, and from two the eggs were stolen. Total increase 0.

In 1909 six nests were known, and a seventh pair of birds were observed in another part of Wales. Only one pair succeeded in hatching two young ones, and of these only one was successfully reared. Total increase one.

It would thus be seen that the strenuous efforts made to preserve the British race of Kites had not been in vain and that, at the present time, the total number had increased to about fifteen. This success was largely due to the energy displayed by Lord Cawdor, who, at his own expense, had furnished watchers to guard the nests on his estates.

The Chairman moved that a special vote of thanks from the Members of the Club should be accorded not only to Lord Cawdor, but also to Mr Meade-Waldo, the treasurer of the Kite Fund, who had supplied a considerable portion of the funds and had likewise been largely instrumental in saving the remnant of our British Kites from extermination.

This motion was seconded and carried unanimously. The Secretary was instructed to write to both these gentlemen in the above sense.

From the report of the Club's meeting on 19 October 1910.

Mr E.G.B. Meade-Waldo (the treasurer of the Kite Fund) stated that the breeding season of the Kite (*Milvus milvus*) being now over, he thought that the Members of the Club might care to hear some details of what had taken place in Wales during 1910. So far as he had been able to ascertain, the facts were as follows: Of the four nests which had been watched, three contained young, which were successfully reared. One nest had three young ones, another two, and a third one; the fourth nest was forsaken during incubation. The nest in which only one young bird was reared originally contained two nestlings, but one of these, which had apparently been blown out of the nest during a violent storm, had been found dead at the foot of the tree.

It had been suggested that the stock of British Kites still existing in Wales had probably become infertile through old age and interbreeding, but this appeared to be by no means the case: on the contrary, they seemed to be remarkably fertile, only one addled egg having been found in the nests that were examined in 1910. The number of birds now appeared to be about twenty, and it was gratifying to be able to record the appearance this autumn of a pair nearly thirty miles from their headquarters. Every precaution was being taken to preserve them from destruction.

Mr Meade-Waldo added that it was now five years since he had asked the Members of the Club for pecuniary help towards the expenses incurred in preserving these remarkably interesting and beautiful birds of prey, but he was now about to beg for further assistance.

This appeal was generously responded to, and a considerable sum was collected in the room. Further sums are, however, urgently wanted, and subscriptions may be forwarded to the treasurer of the fund.

From the report on the Club's meeting on 11 December 1912.

Mr E.G.B. Meade-Waldo (treasurer of the Kite Fund) made the following statement:

At the commencement of the recent nesting-season we knew of ten pairs of Kites, and nests of nine pairs were located. Of this number three pairs successfully reared broods of three, two, and two young respectively; three nests were taken, and one, in a new locality, contained addled eggs, probably due to over-zeal on the part of the watchers. An eighth nest was forsaken, and the ninth was blown out of the tree. The tenth pair, whose nest was not found, hatched and certainly reared one young bird, which was frequently seen.

It is remarkable that none of the Kites which lost their eggs laid a second clutch; and, although they were frequently seen carrying nesting-materials, they never settled down. On the whole the past season has been a good one, but it might have been much better; and if next season proves successful, the British race of Kites will no longer be in danger of extinction, and the birds ought soon to spread back into some of their former haunts.

From the report on the Club's meeting on 9 October 1918.

Mr Meade-Waldo gave the following account of the efforts that have been made in recent years to preserve the native stock of Kites in Wales:

I took over the secretaryship of the BOU Kite Protection Fund from Mr Witherby in 1905. As far as I could make out from my own observations, and from what the local residents and those interested in their preservation told me, there were then only two pairs of old birds and possibly one odd male. In the summer of 1906 both these pairs successfully reared two young ones each. Since then, with much careful watching, the Kites have steadily increased, but, until quite lately, very slowly. I have given no report since I last asked for subscriptions in 1910, as no doubt the less said about them the better during these years. I have visited the area annually, and have been able to make the following notes on the habits of these Welsh Kites. They are remarkably tame, and almost invariably nest close to a farm or cottage. The nest is almost always in an oak tree, probably because the hillsides are largely covered with oak woods, the trees being usually of small size. The only two exceptions were a nest built in a straggling larch tree in a stackyard close to a house (this nest contained only one young) and a nest built in a solitary birch tree, from which three young flew.

As in all raptorial birds, the cock does the whole of the foraging until the young leave the nest, and generally hunts far away from the nest – often seven or eight miles. The food is very varied, and consists of young rabbits, the remains of animals found dead; in spring pieces of lamb, generally the head, occasional chickens, goslings, and many young rooks taken from the nest, snakes, adders, and also quite small objects, probably worms, for I could not see what they were, although quite close to the nest. On one occasion the skin of a hedgehog filled the middle of the nest, with three full-grown young Kites sitting around it!

Although these Kites have been inbred for so many years their eggs are remarkably fertile, a clear egg being very uncommon. Except man, their chief enemy seems to be the Carrion-crow, which is extremely common in Wales. These combine to try and make the old bird leave her eggs.

The same nest appears to be rarely re-occupied, but a new nest is built in the same quarter of the wood. Some strange material is often added to the lining, such as rags, paper, and often a piece of rope. Kites do not seem to object to Buzzards nesting near them. On one occasion, when standing close to two Buzzards' nests, each containing full-grown young, two pairs of old Buzzards soared over 'mewing' and making fine stoops at me, nearly reaching the tree-tops. A Kite came and made repeated and splendid slanting stoops at the Buzzards, but took not the slightest notice of me, although she had young just out of the nest close by. During the winter the Kites congregate at roosting-time, several (as many as thirty) in a sycamore tree in a farm square. In early spring they soar at a great height in small lots of five or seven together.

* * *

One of the most striking features in the fascinating accounts of the BOC's attempts to protect the residual pairs of Kites in the first two decades of this century, is how little the nature of the problems has changed in the intervening years up to the present! The annual depredations of egg collectors continue to frustrate the best efforts of nest protection, and bad weather, predators and other unattributable factors regularly add to the catalogue of nest failures. Dr Salter proposed the active watching of nests round the clock in 1903. In 1992 the same measure is still necessary – even if assisted by a platoon of Gurkhas nowadays! – and collectors will now operate under cover of night as well as the more traditional times of dusk and dawn. The Rev. F.C.R. Jourdain, as we can see, was prominent in the attempt to afford protection to the Kite although he too could not resist the lure of helping himself to a clutch in the years before his active participation in protection. In 1903 the Club resolved to raise a fund to 'procure the conviction, etc.' but it was not until 1971 that a case against an egg collector was first taken to court. Bounties to landowners and payments to watchers or keepers were instituted as long ago as the 1890s and have continued to be paid by the RSPB without break from 1922 to 1992.

The Rev. Edmondes Owen questioned why the Kite (amongst others) favoured mid-Wales and not the more rugged areas of Snowdonia. It is easy to point out that it was only by dint of fortune and remoteness that mid-Wales was the one small area where the Kite was not finally exterminated and thus managed to hang on in hidden valleys. However, it is also probably true that it was never particularly common in Snowdonia. Certainly, nowadays, it is much more successful in the lower, less mountainous parts of mid-Wales where farmland is more productive and a wider variety of food is available; the Red Kite is not exclusively the carrion feeder it is often deemed to be. Edmondes Owen also mentioned the problem of corvid predation on nests: this remains a problem, perhaps reaching it zenith in 1991 when a pair of Ravens slew the male Kite in its nesting tree after the brood of young Ravens had chanced to settle in the same tree.

At the same meeting Mr Gwynne Vaughan instanced problems of nest failure due to both infertility and unexplained dead young. Between 1989 and 1992 the RSPB operated a research programme through the use of tiny video cameras at nests, looking at the self-same problem of why so many nests fail for unexplained reasons; fratricide, probably linked to food shortage, is now known to be a considerable factor, as is poor weather, poor parenthood and mischance (eggs pierced by adult talons, young choking on live frog, etc.). The Kites often seem beset by inefficiency and bad fortune. Infertility has been a popular theory for many years and recent DNA work from blood samples indicates a narrower genetic pool than might be expected from a healthy wild population. However, productivity from an increasing number of Welsh pairs is now good and infertility cannot be regarded as a seriously restraining factor.

Gwynne Vaughan also related how a clutch of deserted eggs was taken in 1909 and placed in an incubator. (They failed to hatch and embryos had clearly died in the intervening period.) Since 1987 the NCC (now Countryside Council for Wales) and the RSPB have pursued a policy of taking deserted or vulnerable clutches for artificial incubation and subsequent return of chicks to the wild. The success rate of this operation has been high and has deprived egg collectors of several clutches as well as helping other, 'failed' nests to be productive; but it took 78 years, since Gwynne Vaughan's report, for the process to be seriously and scientifically approached.

The meeting of the BOC in February 1903 decided to appoint 'a Kite Committee ... to take steps to procure the preservation of the Kite ...' For 89 uninterrupted years this committee has continued to exist, albeit in everchanging form, comprising local people and national figures (latterly paid professionals as well), all dedicated to the cause of the Red Kite. It is a unique arrangement, not always harmonious over the years, which has no parallel in the annals of bird protection anywhere in the world. Its genesis lies firmly in the actions of BOC almost ninety years ago.

ROGER LOVEGROVE

Egg-collecting

In the early years of the century the Club's members included a number of very keen egg-collectors, headed by the controversial figure of P.F. Bunyard, who over the years exhibited a very large number of his specimens at the Club's meetings. It is apparent that some of the more scientifically minded and conscientious of the leading members of the Club were becoming increasingly unhappy with the state of affairs; with increasing awareness of the need for conservation, the scientific value of most egg-collecting was being called into question, and the Club's reputation was in danger of being compromised. The first indication in the *Bulletin* that all was not well appears in the account of the Club's meeting on 19 October 1910. One suspects that 'a somewhat animated discussion' is something of an under-statement.

Bunyard, however, was not unduly dismayed. At any rate, he continued to exhibit his specimens regularly. He often clashed with that *Pastor pugnax*, the Rev. F.C.R. Jourdain, another leading egg-collector, as related in the account of the meeting on 14 January 1920, which also illustrates the rather tenuous scientific justification which oologists tried to make of their hobby. Bunyard's claim, based on eggs, that the Hobby had bred in Ireland has not been upheld.

Matters finally came to a head at the Club's meeting on 12 April 1922. The keen oologists among the BOC's members were also members of the Oological Club. Although this body had no formal connection with the BOU or BOC, for a number of years the *Bulletin* had included reports of the 'Oological Dinners', which were a great feature of the Oological Club's acti-vities. Large numbers of eggs were exhibited at these dinners, and the *Bul-letin* reports gave full details. At the BOC meeting on 12 April 1922, not long after the 11th Oological Dinner, the BOC finally put its house in order.

From the report on the Club's meeting on 19 October 1910.

Mr P.F. Bunyard exhibited a series of eggs, including abnormally marked examples of the following species: Song-thrush (*Turdus musicus*) (a clutch of four eggs with the ground-colour pure white); Stonechat (*Pratincola rubicola*) (clutch of five eggs with the ground-colour green, as in the eggs of the Pied Flycatcher); Ringed Plover (*Aegialitis hiaticola*); Nightjar (*Caprimulgus europ-aeus*); Lesser Whitethroat (*Sylvia curruca*); and Wood-lark (*Lullula arborea*).

He also showed a clutch of eight eggs of the Long-eared Owl (*Asio otus*) and a clutch of eggs taken in Lancashire on the 20th of April 1910, and believed to be those of the Ruff (*Machetes pugnax*). They had been sent to him as eggs of the Common Snipe (*Gallinago gallinago*), but he considered them to be undoubtedly those of the Ruff.

The Chairman said that he would be glad to hear any comments on Mr Bunyard's exhibit, and called on Mr J.L. Bonhote, who made the following remarks:

I hardly like to rise in order to object to exhibitions that Members at much personal inconvenience have been good enough to bring here to show us; but it seems to me that we are hardly fair to ourselves if we let displays, such as Mr Bunyard has brought before us tonight, pass without comment. We are all, with the exception of a few guests, Members of the BOU, and two years ago the BOU passed a rule condemning the taking or destroying of rare British birds and their eggs. To go back still further, this very Club passed some years ago a pious expression of opinion that its Members should stay their hand in regard to the destruction of certain species; yet we now find ourselves looking on, if not with enthusiasm, at least with that silence which gives consent, at a display of clutches of eggs of several distinctly local birds and the exhibition of an extremely rare clutch of eggs, in the taking of which, I am glad to note, the exhibitor had no share, though we must always bear in mind that eggs would not be taken if there was no market for them.

I am the last to decry collecting: how many of us owe our interest in birds to the egg-collections we made as boys at school, and where would our knowledge of the science of ornithology be were it not for collections? But the good of collecting lies in its use and not in its abuse, and I do not hesitate to say that no scientific purpose is served by the accumulation of masses of clutches or by the destruction of a single clutch of one or our very rare breeding species. Such acts only pander to a collector's greed, and bring the scientific study of birds into bad repute. Since our last meeting in June a letter, which some of you may have seen, appeared in *The Times* from a former Member, decrying the present attitude of the union and stating that it had become a society of exterminating collectors. Such remarks as this, which tend to injure our whole status, must be refuted in no uncertain manner, and if we continue to witness exhibitions such as the present without a protest we are certainly adding an appearance of truth to such remarks.

All I would ask you tonight is to show by a motion your strong disapproval of the mere collectors' and exterminators' instinct which leads to exhibitions like the present; and I would therefore beg leave to move the following resolution:

> That this Meeting strongly disapproves of the collecting and exhibiting of large series of clutches of eggs of British breeding birds, or of British-taken eggs of our rare breeding species, except for the purpose of demonstrating some new scientific fact.

Mr Meade-Waldo said that he would be most happy to second the motion, which, after a somewhat animated discussion in which a number of Members took part, was carried almost unanimously.

From the report on the Club's meeting on 14 January 1920.

Mr P.F. Bunyard exhibited a large series of eggs of the Kestrel and the Hobby to illustrate his remarks in reply to certain criticisms on the clutch of eggs from Ireland, which he believed were those of the Hobby, exhibited at the last meeting. He had brought up this series, he said, in order to show how dissimilar the two were when a large series of each were placed side by side. To his eyes they did not present a single similar character. He had never yet seen a well-authenticated clutch of Hobbies' eggs which could possibly be confused with those of the Kestrel, and in ninety-nine cases out of a hundred they could easily be picked out by an experienced oologist, and he would consider the time he had spent on the study of oology wasted if he could not do so. He considered that the fundamental aim of scientific oology should be the identification of eggs at sight, and could not see the use of weights and measurements if they could not be relied upon to assist in ident-ification. The grain of the shell alone was sufficient in some cases for identifi-cation, and especially so with eggs of the Hobby. He pointed out that Newton had called special attention to the grain of the egg-shell and to the investigations carried out by Drs Landois, and Rudolph Blasius, and mentions that even specific differences are apparent in the eggs of certain Swans and Geese. The speaker had made the interesting discovery that eggs of the Pink-footed Goose had a very marked specific difference in grain.

Mr Bunyard went on to say that, providing a sufficiently large series of well-authenticated specimens of a species were available to work upon, there should be no difficulty in fixing the type, and when once this had been estab-lished the practised eye should be able to fix the parentage. He considered it remarkable that some ornithologists could recognise the minutest superficial differences in subspecies and yet were unable to do so with oological speci-mens. An objection had been raised because the Irish clutch which he believed to belong to the Hobby consisted of four, and with reference to Mr Hale's challenge he had written to his friend Mr John Palmer of Ludlow, who had had unique experience with this species and had probably seen more clutches of its eggs *in situ* than anyone else. Mr Palmer replied to the effect that out of thirty clutches of Hobbies' eggs taken by himself four had consisted of four, these being in his opinion the product of the same bird. Amongst the series exhibited was a clutch of four taken in Surrey on July 4th, 1904, the bird having been shot at the nest. There was also a record in the *Birds of Hampshire* of a clutch of four taken on June 2nd, 1884, and also a clutch of five in June 1894.

As regards the date of the Irish clutch, May 31st, he did not consider this too early for Ireland, because he found that other species bred at least ten to fourteen days earlier there than in England, he referred especially to the Grasshopper Warbler and Common Bunting.

The Rev. F.C.R. Jourdain, referring to Mr Bunyard's statement that he could tell Hobbies' from Kestrels' eggs in ninety-nine cases out of a hundred, produced a case of eggs of these two birds, and asked Mr Bunyard to identify them. Mr Bunyard at first said he would do so if he might be allowed to take them home for a week, weigh them, and examine them by daylight, but upon Mr Jourdain agreeing to allow him to do this, he declined to have anything to do with them.

From the report on the Club's meeting on 12 April 1922.

Before the commencement of the ordinary business of the Club, the Chairman announced that previous to the dinner a meeting of the committee had been held in order to decide what action should be taken in regard to the transactions of the Oological Club. After some discussion it was decided that, as the British Ornithologists' Club was in no way responsible for the proceedings of the Oological Club, it was undesirable that these should be published in the *Bulletin* in future.

The Chairman further stated that this question had been raised in consequence of some remarks made by Earl Buxton at a recent meeting of the Royal Society for the Protection of Birds, when he (Lord Buxton) criticised with considerable warmth some of the exhibitions of large series of clutches of eggs exhibited at the Oological Dinners and reported in the *Bulletin*.

Lord Buxton's remarks were brought to the notice of the Committee of the Union, and the following letter, signed by the President and Secretary of the Union on behalf of the Committee, appeared in *The Times* of the 10th April:

WILD BIRD PROTECTION
To the Editor of *The Times*
Sir, In consequence of the exhibition of some clutches of wild birds' eggs at the last Oological dinner, Lord Buxton, at the annual meeting of the Royal Society for the Protection of Birds, drew public attention to the action of certain oologists as constituting a distinct menace to the effective protection of wild birds and to the due enforcement of the laws passed for their protection. Lord Buxton forwarded a copy of his speech to the British Ornithologists' Union for their observations.

In the first place, the Committee of the BOU would point out that the Oological dinners are not held under the auspices of the British Ornithologists' Union, nor are those who attend necessarily members either of the BO Union or the BO Club. In view, however, of the public interest in the question of the protection of wild birds and of their eggs, the Committee of the BOU desire publicly to state (as they have already assured Lord Buxton):

(1) That they are desirous of encouraging the protection of rare birds in England in every way possible;

(2) That it is their ambition to limit the collecting of eggs to the taking of such as are required in the interests of science, and they specially protest against the taking of eggs of any birds in any locality where they are rare, or the taking of eggs in unnecessary numbers;

(3) That it is their emphatic desire to support, both in letter and in spirit, the Acts which provide for the protection of birds and their eggs, and they deprecate very strongly the action of any member who disobeys these laws, or who incites any other to break or evade them.

We are, Sir, yours faithfully,

H.J. Elwes, President, BOU
E.C. Stuart Baker, Hon. Secretary, BOU
British Ornithologists' Union,
6 Harold Road, Upper Norwood, SE 19.

The Committee of the British Ornithologists' Club desire to associate themselves in every way with the principles and views laid down in the letter, and feel that under these circumstances they can no longer continue to publish in the *Bulletin* the proceedings of the Oological Dinners, over which they have no control and for which they are in no way responsible.

Bird exploitation and conservation at home and abroad

Although the Club's main practical efforts were put into saving the Red Kite in Wales, from the end of the last century other aspects of conservation were aired at its meetings, from general concern about the over-exploitation of bird populations to nest-boxes and other ways of counteracting the increasing impoverishment of the natural environment (here Hartert foreshadowed an approach later taken up very effectively by the RSPB), the export of live birds from Africa (still a major abuse, now needing international action), and an early attempt to assess bird casualties on roads (to be the subject of a BTO inquiry a few years later – *Bird Study* 12 (1965): 90–99). It does not seem to be recorded that any member of the BOU was ever 'visited with the severest censure' for persecuting rare birds, as proposed by Meade-

Waldo in 1900. The final item, the 'Controversial Discussion', records an attempt to introduce some variety into the Club's meetings. This was not repeated, perhaps because no other subject could be expected to elicit such forthright and often conflicting opinions.

From the report on the Club's meeting on 19 April 1899.

Mr Sclater stated that he had been staying in the Riviera during the past four weeks, and wished to call attention to the appalling deficiency of bird-life in that otherwise charming country. Although out every day on the hills round Cannes and Nice, and always on the look-out, he had seen but very few birds, and those mostly of the commonest sorts and always shy and timid. Even Sparrows were only occasionally to be met with. In the beautifully kept gardens of the villas not a bird's note was to be heard, and very rarely was a single Tit or Robin to be seen. Mr Sclater attributed this scarcity of birds (which was deplorable, not only from an aesthetic but still more from an economical point of view) to the prevalence of the '*chasse*' during the autumn and winter months and the sale of small birds of every sort for food in the markets; and expressed a hope that every Member of the BOU would do all he could to shelter and protect bird-life in the country, lest we should fall into the same condition.

From the report on the Club's meeting on 21 February 1900.

Mr Ernst Hartert showed some nesting-boxes for the encouragement of birds which breed in holes. Mr Hartert stated that he had very little faith in the customary methods of bird protection, which consisted of praising and over-rating the usefulness of birds, and of advocating more and more stringent bird protection laws.

There was, however, another kind of bird protection, which might be called 'practical' protection. This originated from the understanding that it was not generally the killing of certain birds that made many of our species become scarcer, but the progress of cultivation of the ground, the careful keeping of our gardens, modern forestry, and similar reasons. All these causes were diminishing the nesting opportunities of many birds and their supply of natural food. Therefore the 'practical' bird protection, which was so warmly advocated on the Continent by Freiherr von Berlepsch, aimed at nothing less than to furnish new breeding-places for useful birds, natural food in hard winter-times, and cover and protection against their enemies. The feeding in winter-time was not so easy, and one might read Berlepsch's book on this subject with advantage. The planting of thick bushes, especially those with thorns and berry-bearing species as were liked by birds, instead of the foreign evergreens and shrubs which only a few birds really loved, was not within the means of every one, and could only be done by landowners who were interested in birds; but the putting up of nesting-boxes could be done almost everywhere, in gardens, parks, and woods, on a large or small scale. In Germany, nesting-boxes were a very old institution, but they had never met with general approval, as they had never been quite successful. Now, however, von Berlepsch had invented nesting-boxes like those exhibited, and they were a most wonderful success. They were imitations of Woodpecker's holes, and were readily accepted by birds, especially by Tits. They must, however, be put up properly, and in Berlepsch's book on bird-protection some good instructions were given. Mr Charles Rothschild and Mr Walter Rothschild had introduced them on a small scale in various places, and Mr Hartert hoped to be able to report concerning their success during the next session of the Club, and he trusted that other ornithologists would advocate them. They were made in great numbers, and could be had for about sixpence each, from a firm in Westphalia, who were making them according to Berlepsch's instruction.

From the report on the Club's meeting on 16 May 1900.

Mr Meade-Waldo called the attention of the Union to the way in which rare species of birds were still being persecuted or destroyed in Great Britain. He felt sure that no member of the Union would willingly assist in bringing about this lamentable occurrence, but that in consideration of the persistency with which all our rare breeding birds were annually harried by British egg-collectors, and on that account the great difficulty, if not impossibility, experienced by landed proprietors in preserving them, he considered that the time had come to make a supreme effort. He proposed the following resolution, which was seconded by Mr H.M. Upcher, and carried unanimously:

> That any member of the Union, directly or indirectly responsible for the destruction of nest, eggs, young, or parent-birds of any of the species mentioned below – Osprey, Kite, White-tailed Eagle, Honey Buzzard, Common Buzzard, Hoopoe, Golden Oriole, Ruff, Bittern, and Chough – should be visited with the severest censure of the Union.

A discussion ensued, in which the President and other members took part.

The Hon. G. Lascelles gave an interesting account of the efforts made by the Crown for the preservation of the birds in the New Forest. He lamented that, in spite of the strenuous efforts made, the keepers were only partially successful, although men were specially told to guard the nesting-place of some rare species. He was pleased to say, however, that on some occasions their efforts had been rewarded with success.

From the report on the Club's meeting on 17 October 1900.

Mr Meade-Waldo gave some interesting experiences of the nesting-boxes put up on his estate in Kent. He found that they were practically never used by Sparrows, if placed low down and away from houses. The SW was found to be the worst exposure for the boxes, the best height for which was from four to six feet from the ground. A heavy lid that will open enables the boxes to be cleaned and the old nests taken out every year, a few holes being pierced in the bottom of the box for draining purposes. The heavy solid boxes must be fixed firmly.

Four species of Tits used these boxes, but 80 per cent of the number were occupied by Blue and Great Tits, the latter predominating. Occasionally, however, the case was reversed, and Blue Tits were the predominating occupants. Wrynecks used them often, preferring boxes in open situations, and a pair of these birds would often devastate a number of Tits' nests, without using the boxes themselves. Nuthatches frequently availed themselves of the boxes, plastering the holes round with mud as well as the inside of the lid after the box had been fastened down. This year (1900) they took to the boxes so freely that out of 25 within a limited area no less than 17 were occupied by them.

Large boxes fixed in trees at from 20 to 30 feet from the ground, of the size of 20 inches square, with a double-span roof, and a projecting eave of about 4 inches over the hole, were occupied by Barn- and Tawny Owls, Jackdaws, Stock-doves, and Kestrels, while Squirrels and Stoats occasionally took them. Kestrels were the prevailing birds this year, no fewer than five pairs nesting round one field, in which about 1,000 young Pheasants were reared, and the Hawks never touched any of the latter, though they passed over the field repeatedly in all directions. Mr Meade-Waldo would not imply that Kestrels did not occasionally take young Pheasants from the coops, but as voles swarmed throughout the nesting season in some of the young plantations, the Kestrels doubtless found abundance of their favourite food. All these Kestrels disappeared about the beginning of August, after which time scarcely a bird was to be seen. Many other species of birds occupied boxes occasionally; though there were practically unlimited nesting-sites in the neighbourhood, but few boxes were left untenanted.

Egret farms in India

From the report on the Club's meeting on 9 June 1920.

Dr C.B. Ticehurst also called attention to the recent statements made (in Parliament and in the press) regarding Egret farms in India in connection with the Plumage Bill, and made the following observations:

I have seen it stated that no serious naturalist believes in the existence of these farms, and if birds are kept at all in captivity it is done as a cloak to show European officials. These statements are entirely erroneous. Everyone who takes any interest in these matters, as well as ordinary sportsmen, are in Sind, perfectly well acquainted with the existence of these Egret farms, and there is no shadow of doubt about their existence. When I was stationed at Karachi I made a good many inquiries concerning them, and gathered a good bit of information concerning them. Since nearly all are situated in the exactly opposite corner of Sind to Karachi, and in very inaccessible places, I did not personally have the pleasure of inspecting them myself. But my friend Mr Gordon, Canal Engineer at Jacobabad and later at Mirpurkhas, has visited one or more farms on several occasions, and at my request did so again, to get answers to my queries on the subject on the spot. Full details of the Egret Farms in Sind will be given in my forthcoming paper on the Birds of Sind, but I will give now just a short *resumé* of it. The birds kept are said to have come originally from Bahawalpur district at the commencement of the industry fifteen to sixteen years ago. They are kept in reed-screen huts with full use of wings and eyes; in the huts native beds (charpoys) are put, on which the birds breed in colonies, sticks being put into the aviary for nest purposes. The huts are 70 feet by 35 feet, holding 300 birds. Several families are employed catching fish for the birds, tending them, and keeping off jackals and foxes, etc. The young reared in captivity go towards increasing the stock. The plumes appear about March, and these are pulled out about July, two pluckings of plumes take place in summer and two in winter. The plumes are graded, the best fetch about 200 rupees per tola.

The killing of Egrets, and then the catching of live birds and sewing up their eyes, was put a stop to years ago by the order of Sir Evan James, then Commissioner in Sind, and I can confidently say that no Egrets are nowadays shot in Sind – indeed, very few Sindhis are allowed the use of firearms.

The exportation of Egret plumes has been stopped, but I understand the plumes from Sind are sold in India to various royal households.

Obviously the plucking of plumes does not affect the birds much or they would cease to breed, which they do not, as two or three broods are reared each year by taking away the young and hand-rearing them.

A small bunch of plumes was handed round for inspection. An account, perfectly genuine with genuine photographs of the Sind Egret farms, appeared in the Bombay Natural History Society's *Journal* some years ago by Mr Birch.

The exportation of live birds from Africa

From the report on the Club's meeting on 11 May 1927.

Mr Bannerman drew attention to the very unsatisfactory methods employed in the export trade of small brightly coloured Weavers and other birds from Senegal for sale in Europe. Hundreds of these birds were shipped at Dakar on the liner in which he travelled to Marseilles, and the condition of these birds called forth protests from every humane passenger on board. The birds were crammed into long cages or wooden crates with wire fronting some 4 ft × 2 × 1½ in size, over a hundred in each cage – the floor-space and inadequate perches filled to overflowing with fluttering birds struggling to gain a foothold. These birds, mostly the commoner small Weavers, were all freshly netted wild birds, and their fruitless efforts to gain their liberty added to the heavy mortality which must have taken place. The whole enormous consignment was in charge of one native boy sent from Dakar. The crates were piled on the aft hatch under a tarpaulin which had to be removed in port, and the conditions of feeding, watering, and protection from the weather left much to be desired. Particularly distressing was the case of a Woolly-necked Stork confined in a small wooden box without room to stretch up its neck.

Mr Bannerman spoke very strongly on the unnecessary cruelty entailed. He said he was far from wishing the export of foreign birds prohibited, but he pleaded for a much more rigorous control of the manner in which our foreign cage-birds reached Europe.

A discussion followed and Major Flower, late Director of the Giza Gardens, Egypt, Dr Casey Wood of the USA, Mr Gerard Gurney, a well-known aviculturist, and others spoke of similar experiences, and urged that steps should be taken to mitigate this state of affairs.

It was agreed that Mr Bannerman should be asked to report to the International Committee for the Protection of Birds, who would, it was hoped, take the matter up.

Bannerman's report elicited the following from Captain C.R.S. Pitman, Game Warden, Uganda (from the Bulletin *published 12 October 1927).*

I was much interested in the May number of the *Bulletin* to read Mr D.A. Bannerman's remarks in regard to the unnecessary cruelty with which live birds are exported to the United Kingdom and Europe from West Africa. I recently travelled from Mombasa to Marseilles in a steamer which was carrying several hundreds of birds and a few mammals for zoological dealers and others.

As Game Warden of Uganda, and in co-operation with the game wardens of the other British Territories in Eastern Africa, I spare no efforts to discourage all forms of collecting live animals for export, and collecting agents receive scant sympathy, as it is well known that the first cardinal principle of game preservation is the fact that no profit should be made out of game.

In this connection, I have had a good deal of correspondence with a certain British importer, and I was amazed to find that animals collected for this individual were apparently consigned to him by ship without any adequate arrangements being made for the comfort of the captives. By this I mean that a collection of about 770 Love-birds were crushed into ten small wooden cases with wire fronts. The birds were just jammed into a solid mass, those nearest the grain and water troughs obtained sustenance – as for the rest, they starved! Originally, there were so many birds in each box that many had to stand on each other. The boxes were so low that the struggling inmates continually bruised their heads, eventually knocking off all their feathers and damaging their crowns. Such birds were killed by their neighbours. There were no facilities for cleaning the cages, and the condition of the birds in tropical temperatures was deplorable. This collection was handed over to the captain of the ship, who was asked to look after and feed the animals and to hand them over to the importer's representative at Marseilles. I am not certain at which port this collection was shipped, but before we left Mombasa nearly half the unfortunate birds had perished, this in spite of the fact that the captain had made arrangements for the ship's carpenter to make a number of additional and more roomy cages, and the remnants of the luckless birds were housed in fully sixteen boxes.

I understand that such happenings are of no unusual occurrence, and it seems to me high time that drastic steps were taken to ensure fair treatment to such helpless captives.

Bird protection in Greenland

From Col. R. Meinertzhagen's account of the birds of Greenland, 17 January 1956.

The slaughter of birds in Greenland by the Greenlanders is appalling and in several cases species are nearing extinction. This is due to four main causes. Cheap guns and ammunition, desire for any form of meat and the abundance of small boats with motor engines. In addition, very little attention is paid to protective legislation, though very little of this exists.

As examples of senseless slaughter I quote the following cases which came under my personal observation.

In June, I found a heap of over fifty King Eider on a sandspit; these were just left as the party had shot more than they could carry. Again in Disko Fjord on two occasions in July we saw small boats loaded with Common and King Eider, over fifty in each boat. The Eider during the moulting season are particularly vulnerable as they are close-packed and flightless, being easily driven ashore by boats and then despatched.

The large tern colony at Flakkerhuk produced one young bird out of many thousands of pairs; all the eggs had been taken.

When we landed on Green Islands where there is a huge ternery, our men commenced to take every egg they could find though they were all on the point of hatching. Our efforts to stop them were just laughed at.

At Umanak nearly every house had quantities of Eider and Guillemot hanging outside in the middle of the breeding season.

When we visited a Cormorant rookery in Disko Fjord the three Greenlanders on board commenced to shoot the chicks from the boat without a hope of recovering them and just left dead and wounded to rot.

We found Greenlanders utterly callous to suffering. They will bite off and swallow the orange knob at the base of a King Eider's bill when the bird was still alive. Gangs of small boys wander about near settlements when the young of Snow Bunting, Wheatear and Lapland Bunting are fledged, hunt them to death with stones and when the bird is caught the guts are bitten out and swallowed before the bird is dead and the chick then stuffed into a pocket.

Dr Salomonsen has suggested the following remedies (*Dansk. Orn. Foren. Tids.* XLIX. 1955 p. 11).

(a) Protection of all rookeries of Brunnich's Guillemot and restricted egg collecting.
(b) Close season for cormorants.
(c) No egg collecting at terneries after June 30th.
(d) A ten-year absolute protection for the Puffin.

I discussed this problem with Dr Salomonsen in Copenhagen as I do not think his proposals go far enough.

The Greenlanders have for centuries depended on birds as an important food supply; but that is no argument for endangering that same food supply. Also it cannot be too strongly emphasised that birds are not the property of the country where they breed. Birds are international property and it is the duty of every state to preserve bird life and prevent excessive destruction.

I would, in all humility suggest:

(a) That a high purchase tax be placed on all firearms and ammunition so that shooting beyond needs becomes an expensive luxury.
(b) That the taking of eggs of all birds is prohibited after June 15th and that the killing of adults is prohibited on the breeding grounds.
(c) That certain large breeding colonies enjoy absolute protection from any kind of disturbance.
(d) That some official be appointed whose duty is to enforce the law of bird protection and ensure that culprits are adequately punished.
(e) That education includes teaching the young that cruelty is one of the worst human vices.

Bird casualties on roads

From the Bulletin *published 31 December 1956.*

Mr Gerald Finnis read a paper on the above subject at the September meeting, an account of which follows:

When the number of bird casualties found on roads particularly during early summer made it almost possible for me to support a captive Little Owl, I decided to study this subject more carefully. Most of my records were obtained during cycle rides, when it is much easier to stop and collect corpses or make notes on smears indicating a fatality, although I also try to observe the behaviour of species when I am driving.

The following examples of road behaviour were cited: The weak flight of thrushes and blackbirds from low cover flanking roads without a path was a frequent cause of death and in one of his letters (27 June 1923) the late Col. T.E. Lawrence describes an incident when a thrush hit his side-car and he overturned the combination in a vain effort to avoid it. Blackbirds and robins are feeders in the leaf litter of roads during late autumn and winter and although the blackbird is often killed then, the robin generally manages to escape, its peak accident rate being later in the year. Thrushes, particularly during drought periods, hunt for snails in hedge banks and use the road as an anvil.

Grit is a necessity to many species and I have notes of house sparrows frequenting iron gratings from which snow had disappeared and where grit was exposed. A further example of this habit was illustrated during the winter of 1938 when a massive movement of larks crossed Kent and scores of birds alighted in the streets of towns to take grit before feeding in gardens and allotments. Mr George Edwards in a broadcast talk referred to grit being taken by a winter roost of rooks before they passed on to forage in the fields. The carrion crow has also been observed swallowing grit on roads, but equally interesting is the rapidity with which carcases of diseased rabbits or road casualties in other mammals were dealt with by parties of foraging crows.

There do not appear to be any recent notes on nightjars behaving in this country as they do in other parts of the world where they become frequent road casualties. The correspondence relating to this behaviour being found in *The Ibis*, Vol. 96, Nos. 2 and 4, and Vol. 97, No. 2.

Other attractions the roads have for birds are obviously where drinking pools collect and soft mud patches (becoming increasingly rare) for *hirundines*.

Flying birds, even when not directly menaced by traffic, frequently twist and turn in panic and fly along a road for yards if they happen to be crossing a road when a car or a cyclist is beneath them. I have noticed this behaviour particularly in whitethroats and the goldfinch. Some birds also appear to leave their take-off too late and are run over (I once ran over a juvenile house sparrow in this way). I have received a notification of a wren being drawn on to the road and stunned by the air-flow of a passing car. This bird later recovered.

Summary

Total case histories   274 or 28 species

		Male	Female	Juvenile	
Sparrow	109	40	29	19	June/July
Blackbird	42	18	5	12	First 7 months
Song Thrush	38				May, June, July
Chaffinch	15	5	8		June
Greenfinch	13	8	4	1	June/July
Robin	8				July/August
Whitethroat	7				May/June
Starling	7			1	May/June
Lesser Whitethroat	6				May – on passage
Linnet	6				
Dunnock	5				
Blue Tit	3				
Swallow	2				
Great Tit	2				
Yellowhammer	2				

Single examples of the following have been found or reported: Bittern (Dr J.M. Harrison, personal communication), pheasant, red-necked phalarope (found on Brecon Beacons, personal communication, George Shannon), dunlin (this bird was found near Wrotham and had been ringed near Stavanger, J. Allen, personal communication), little owl, wood pigeon, house martin, wren, mistle-thrush, redwing, corn bunting, tree sparrow, budgerigar.

Dr Jeffery Harrison said he had been struck by the apparent difference in the number of bird road casualties in this country and on the Continent, more casualties being found in this country. In two journeys from Kent to Berkshire this summer, 83 miles distant, 55 birds had been found, made up of 42 house sparrows, 6 blackbirds, 3 song thrushes, 1 rook, 1 jay, 1 yellow bunting and a tame pigeon, the order of frequency corresponding closely with Mr Finnis' findings. On a recent visit to France, only 4 casualties were found over 2,252 miles, in spite of a most careful watch. These were 2 house sparrows, a little and a long-eared owl. Mr David Jones, who travelled 1,140 miles in France in August, found only 8. It seemed possible that the twisting British roads, often enclosed by hedges and carrying a heavy volume of traffic, were more lethal to bird life than the straighter, more open French roads, where traffic is lighter.

Another interesting factor is the widespread habit of birds to come on to the roads at dawn. This is reflected in the species killed and the commonest observed is the house sparrow, but the habit is marked in the thrushes, finches, yellow bunting, starling, robin, skylark, pied wagtail, rook and carrion crow. Fast motoring at this time kills many birds. Whether they are collecting grit or feeding is not determined as yet. Two house sparrows and a blackbird picked up soon after dawn contained grit, a blackbird and a song thrush contained small beetles and earwigs and a house sparrow had corn.

Dr Harrison mentioned crows as road casualties, killed as they fed on rabbits and hedgehogs. He also mentioned a snipe he had seen settle and get run over. It was found to be blind in one eye.

Lord Hurcomb wondered whether the different speeds in France and Britain were reflected in Dr Harrison's figures and whether buzzards were finding a living from bird casualties. He also questioned the effect of headlights on birds.

James Fisher referred to a census made about thirty years ago and which would make an interesting comparison with the present time. He had also observed many birds on the roads soon after dawn and had run over a number himself. Although he thought some were getting grit, others he felt sure were there in order to keep their feet dry when there was a heavy dew in the fields. When studying rooks he had noticed that they arrived in the fields later on such mornings. He also mentioned a turkey buzzard and a great bustard as unusual road casualties.

Miss Longfield wondered if the differences in British and French figures were associated with a smaller bird population in France.

Controversial discussion

The Christmas meeting [1 January 1959] was set aside as 'A Controversial Evening' in which the subject was 'Do nesting birds need protection from egg collectors, ringers, photographers and bird-watchers? Do the contributions to science of these enthusiasts justify the disturbance they cause?'

The prospect of battle brought out an exceptionally large number of Members with the seniors reminiscing about the good old days of full-blooded argument in the Club before ladies were admitted. For the discussion Mr Max Nicholson took the Chair though refuting the suggestion that he was a volunteer for the task.

Professor M.F.M. Meiklejohn opened on behalf of the birds. With a wicked humour and in a spirit of sweet unreasonableness he castigated all who interested themselves in birds as unmitigated nuisances to the birds themselves, differing only in degree from the Tripper in his Ornithological Alphabet who 'planted her stern, onto the nest of a Roseate Tern'. He divided the nuisances into four categories the least harmful of which were the slothful ones who watched birds as a pleasant way of spending a day and who were content with ticking off their species list on long-distance identifications usually provided by someone else. The other three categories were inspired by the less innocuous motives of envy, avarice and ambition. The Enviers were particularly dangerous since they concentrated their attentions on rarities in an attempt to keep up with the Jones's. The Avaricious who sold eggs or information were self-condemned, while among the Ambitious he classed all those struggling to win bars to their BSc's by filling the ornithological journals with papers of statistics which no one ever read to the end. (A later speaker suggested that few people even read the beginning).

Major-General C.B. Wainwright followed. His main plea was that, along with the publicity given to birds by the press and the BBC, an attempt should be made to teach some elementary field craft to would-be watchers. He cited poachers as causing the least disturbance since their livelihood depends on field craft.

Major G. Pye-Smith, representing the Jourdain Society dissociated any members of the Society from Professor Meiklejohn's category of Enviers, since responsible oologists had long realised that nothing was to be learnt from the eggs of rare nesting species in Britain. He also cited the value of bird's nesting, if properly undertaken, as training in natural history for the young. Turning to the attack he wished some of the not always well-informed critics of egg-collectors would direct their energies to preserving the habitats of some nesting birds from the depredations of modern agriculture and land development. He introduced Brigadier E.L. Simson as an ally to demonstrate with an exhibition of some clutches of common birds' eggs that there was still much to be learnt on the causes of variation in egg patterns and sizes.

Captain George Yeates won immediate sympathy for the photographers in disclaiming any desire to contribute to science, though admitting, almost reluctantly, that the introduction of the electronic flash had given scientists a better understanding of the mechanics of flight. He thought that if justification was needed for photography it would be found in the part it had played in encouraging the mounting interest in birds, on which ultimately the survival of many species would depend.

At this point it was unfortunately necessary for the Chairman to leave, not because he feared the meeting might get too hot, but because he had to return to Lydd for another controversial meeting on the future of Dungeness as a nature reserve. This gave him added reason to support wholeheartedly Major Pye-Smith's plea for energy in the preservation of nesting habitats. He reinforced this with an apt plea for more unity among bird-lovers in combatting outside threats to bird life, which momentarily rallied all opposing factions in some semblance of harmony. Advantage was taken of the ensuing lull for a break for refreshment.

When the discussion was resumed the egg collectors took some nasty knocks until Dr W. Serle brought an unexpected champion to their cause, and one moreover not present to be shot at, in showing that Moses had given them their first charter (Deuteronomy 22, verses 6 and 7). Captain C.R.S. Pitman and Dr T. Clay also supported the taxonomic and scientific value of eggs of little-known African birds, and of the specific proteins in egg albumen.

Among other contributions some criticism was directed at the ringing of nestlings which was largely refuted by Mr R. Spencer who showed that the recovery of many birds known to have been ringed in the nest was ample proof that the operation did not lead to the high fatalities suggested, and furthermore was of great value in studying longevity in birds.

The meeting eventually closed in a spirit of seasonal goodwill.

B.P.H.

Ornithologists

The *Bulletin* has not normally published obituaries of its members. This has been left to the journal of the Club's parent body, *The Ibis*. In fact, only one full obituary has appeared, that of Bowdler Sharpe, and a shorter one, of P.L. Sclater, these being perhaps the two most outstanding of the Club's early members.

It used to be the custom for the Chairman, in his annual address, to mention the Members who had died in the past year. A sad feature of these addresses in the years 1915–18 was the names of Club Members and other ornithologists, sometimes on both sides, who had been killed in the past year. Two extracts follow. The war also directly affected the *Bulletin* in another way. At the meeting on 9 June 1915, the Chairman, Lord Rothschild, 'regretted to announce that the Editor – Mr. D.A. Bannerman – was compelled to resign his office at the conclusion of this session, as he was shortly going to France, taking a motor ambulance in the service of the Red Cross'.

From the Chairman's address on 8 December 1915.

Brother Members of the BOC,

Fourteen months ago, when I last addressed you, we were in the throes of the greatest war and, incidentally, the greatest and most tragic catastrophe the world has ever known; unfortunately, when I now come to address you once more, we are still far from seeing peace – in fact, I might almost say as far off as then. This terrible war has not spared our Club, and we all have to regret the personal loss of many friends and also an irreparable loss to our favourite science.

We have to mourn the deaths of Lieutenant R.B. Woosnam, Captain The Hon. Gerald Legge, Major C.H.J. Whitehead, Lord Brabourne, Lieutenant K.J. Meiklejohn, Lieutenant C.M. Dyer, and Lieutenant Lewis N.G. Ramsay. Although not all members of our Club, they were one and all most

183

ardent and indefatigable ornithologists, and their loss is, indeed, a hard one to bear.

Among our allies in France, we have to regret the death from wounds of Prince E. d'Arenberg. On the side of our enemies Herr Geyr von Schweppenburg has lost a leg and Count Zedlitz has also been wounded, while Hermann Löns has been killed.

From the Chairman's address on 10 October 1917.

Brother Members of the BOC,

It is already the fourth session of our Club in which we find ourselves in the midst of the most terrible infliction humanity has ever endured. The past year has seen many and irreparable losses to our Union and Club, due both to the war and natural causes.

Captain John Cyril Crowley, the great-nephew of the late Philip Crowley, a most enthusiastic ornithologist and pre-eminently a bird-photographer, was killed in Mesopotamia in September 1916; we also have to mourn the loss of Canon Scott and Sir Ralph Payne-Gallwey; another loss to science was Roland Trimen, who, although an entomologist, as Curator of the Cape Town Museum did much useful work for ornithology; our most severe loss, both to zoology generally and to our Club, was the death of Captain F.C. Selous; further losses due to the war are those of Captain Lord Lucas and Commander The Hon. R.O.B. Bridgeman; death has also taken from us R.Y. Balston, T.H. Nelson, E.A. Mearns, and F.E.L. Beal, all well known for excellent work in our favourite science. During the present year we have also lost E.P. Ramsay and Adolph Nehrkorn; while the war is responsible for the deaths of Henry Peavot, Lieut. H.E.O. Dixon, Otto Le Roi, and Captain Charlton.

In spite of all the obstacles due to the fearful conflict which has engulfed half the nations of the world, our science has maintained its activity, though of course great explorations have been impossible.

F.C. Selous

From the report on the Club's meeting on 10 January 1917.

The Chairman [H.J. Elwes] referred to the great loss which the Club and the Union had suffered by the death of Capt. F.C. Selous, DSO, killed in action in German East Africa at an age when very few men were physically capable of active military service in a tropical climate.

He personally had never known any man who so well combined the character of the best type of Englishman with the highest qualities of an explorer, big game hunter, field naturalist, and author. His private character as a man endeared him to all who knew him, Boers as well as British. His unrivalled strength of constitution and physique and his indomitable courage and determination had enabled him to survive dangers and hardships such as few men had endured, and his absence at their meetings would be regretted for many years to come. He thought that his memory should be perpetuated by some permanent memorial, in which he believed many members of the Union would desire to take part, in conjunction with other societies to which Capt. Selous belonged.

Two forms suggested themselves for such a memorial. First, the erection of a mural tablet with a portrait in bas-relief, to be erected in the Hall of the British Museum of Natural History, should the Trustees give permission. Secondly, the foundation of a Selous Memorial Medal, to be awarded annually, or at such periods as might be decided, to men who had distinguished themselves in the same fields of activity as Selous himself.*

This proposal was unanimously agreed to by the members present.

The Late Richard Bowdler Sharpe, LLD

The announcement of the death of Dr Richard Bowdler Sharpe, at the age of 62, will cause the greatest regret among the very wide circle of his friends and admirers in all parts of the world; but his loss will be more especially felt and mourned by ornithologists, for they can best appreciate his great talents and extraordinary knowledge of birds.

On the 15th of December, 1909, he attended the dinner and meeting of the British Ornithologists' Club, which was founded by him in 1892, and was then apparently in his usual health and good spirits; but while returning to his house at Chiswick he appears to have contracted a severe chill, which rapidly developed into pleuro-pneumonia and ended fatally on the 25th of December.

Dr Sharpe was born on the 22nd of November, 1847, and was the eldest son of the late Thomas Bowdler Sharpe, well known as the publisher of *Sharpe's London Magazine*. He early displayed an ardent love of natural history, more especially of birds and insects, and, as a boy, much of his spare time was spent in the company of William Briggs (the 'Cookham Natu-

---

*The mural tablet was duly erected, but it seems that the proposal for a Selous Memorial Medal was never implemented. The Selous National Park in Tanzania is his best and most permanent memorial.

ralist'), who was head gardener to Mr de Vitré at Formosa, near Cookham. Under the tuition of this able naturalist and taxidermist he made various excursions to different parts of the coast and formed a mounted collection of British birds, which was eventually presented to the British Museum. His father did not regard his son's love for ornithology with favour, and on completing his education at Peterborough (King's Scholar) and Loughborough Grammar Schools he was packed off to London with a sovereign in his pocket and a letter of introduction to Messrs W.H. Smith & Son. He has often shown the writer the place in Brompton Road, opposite the Oratory, where the heel of one of his boots (his only pair) came off as he walked to London! He entered the publishing house of the above-named firm in 1863, and subsequently worked for a year with the late Mr Bernard Quaritch. In 1867, on the recommendation of Dr Sclater, he was appointed Library-Clerk and subsequently Librarian to the Zoological Society of London and retained that post till 1872. With a fine library thus placed at his command he now found ample opportunity of cultivating his taste for the study of birds and, during his term of office, was able to publish a catalogue of his private collection of African birds and his splendid *Monograph of the Kingfishers*, a work of such excellence that it at once established his reputation as an ornithologist of exceptional ability. He also at this time conceived and, in partnership with Mr H.E. Dresser, commenced to publish a great serial work on the *Birds of Europe*; but after fifteen parts had been issued he was obliged, owing to other important engagements, to relinquish his share of the work, and the remaining parts were completed by Mr Dresser alone.

On the death of George Robert Gray, Dr Sharpe entered the service of the Trustees of the British Museum and was appointed Senior Assistant in the Department of Zoology on the 11th of September, 1872. With his appointment began a new era in the administration of the bird-collection and the *Catalogue of the Birds in the British Museum*, the great work of his life, was commenced. No one of the present generation who visits the bird-room of the Natural History Museum can have any conception of the difficulties under which work was carried on in the old days at the British Museum, Bloomsbury, the underground dungeons which were used as work-rooms being small and very insufficiently lighted. The first volume of the *Catalogue*, containing the birds of prey, was completed and published by the trustees in 1874, and the whole work, contained in twenty-seven thick volumes, took twenty-four years to finish, having been only completed in 1898. Eleven different specialists took part in this laborious undertaking: Dr Sharpe himself contributed no less than eleven whole volumes and portions of three others, and edited or assisted in the preparation of the remainder. These volumes contain a description of every known species of bird up to the date of publication, and Dr Sharpe was justly proud of his large share in the work which he himself had initiated. Only those who have attempted a similar task can appreciate the enormous amount of labour and research, the days and nights of continuous toil, which the production of even one of these volumes entailed.

Dr Sharpe remained Senior Assistant in the Natural History Museum till November 1895, when he was promoted to be Assistant-Keeper in charge of the Vertebrate Section of the Zoological Department, a post which he retained till his death.

During the many years occupied in the preparation of the *Catalogue of Birds* he found time to publish a number of important works, such as the section 'Birds' in the *Zoology of the Voyage of HMS Erebus and Terror*, his *Monograph of Swallows* (with C.W. Wyatt), and to complete the *Birds of Asia*, the *Birds of New Guinea*, and the *Monograph of the Humming-birds*, three great folio works by Gould which had been left unfinished at the time of his death. He also contributed endless important memoirs and papers to various scientific periodicals, more especially to *The Ibis*, the *Journal* and *Transactions of the Linnean Society*, the *Proceedings of the Zoological Society*, and *The Annals and Magazine of Natural History*.

In 1885 Dr Sharpe was sent to India, at the special request of Mr A.O. Hume, to superintend the transport of the unrivalled collection of Indian birds and mammals which had been presented to the British Museum by that gentleman. It contained 63,000 birds, 18,500 eggs, and 500 mammals, all of which were safely packed and brought to South Kensington, a work of no slight difficulty. During his absence the writer was placed in charge of the bird-room and since that date had been closely associated with Dr Sharpe up to the time of his death: he can therefore testify to the fact that the increase and welfare of the collection of birds were always Dr Sharpe's first thought, and he can recollect how, in many instances, when funds were not forthcoming for acquiring valuable specimens, his late colleague purchased them and gave them to the museum.

He was also instrumental in getting many great and valuable collections presented to the nation, for the donors knew that under his charge the specimens would receive the utmost care and be properly dealt with. To give some idea of how the collection increased since he was appointed, I may mention that in 1872 the total number of birds and eggs probably did not exceed 30,000, while at the present time they must number more than 500,000.

Dr Sharpe was elected a Member of the British Ornithologists' Union in 1871, and since that date he had been one of its most active supporters and a frequent contributor to its journal, *The Ibis*. In 1892 he founded the 'British Ornithologists' Club', so that evening meetings might be held once a month from October to June, to promote the discussion of subjects of general interest and to enable members and foreign visitors to exhibit rare and interesting specimens of birds from all parts of the world. The scheme proved an immense success from its commencement, and the proceedings are published in a special *Bulletin*, which was for many years edited by Dr Sharpe.

Between 1899 and 1909 Dr Sharpe compiled a *Hand-list of the Genera and Species of Birds*, which was published by the Trustees of the British Museum in five volumes.

The second volume of the *History of the Collections contained in the Natural History Departments of the British Museum* appeared in 1906, and of this Dr Sharpe wrote the section 'Birds' (pp. 79–515). This very valuable contribution contains many interesting details respecting those who have helped to form the great collection of birds in the Natural History Museum and particulars concerning them, which would otherwise have been lost and forgotten, as many of the facts were based on his personal knowledge of men long since dead and gone.

With the death of Dr Sharpe a link is lost between the modern school of ornithologists and the little band who originally founded the British Ornithologists' Union: he had known them all, and his personal reminiscences, extending over more than forty years, were always interesting and often most entertaining. His extraordinary memory, which enabled him to name collections of birds off-hand with tolerable accuracy, and, by merely glancing over them, to state approximately where they came from, was truly remarkable, especially before his health began to fail and with it his extreme acumen.

During the latter years of his life Dr Sharpe, who had always been a great admirer of Gilbert White, edited a revised edition of the famous *Natural History of Selborne*, with numerous additions and many beautiful plates by Keulemans, which was published by S.T. Freemantle, of Piccadilly, in 1900. He paid many visits to the district of Selborne and became so enamoured of the spot that he purchased a small piece of ground in the neighbourhood and there built himself a cottage in which he and his family spent many happy days.

Dr Sharpe was no mere 'Cabinet-naturalist', as many might suppose, but knew the manners and customs of most of our British birds as well as anyone, being quite as keenly interested in field-work as in the determination of museum specimens.

Dr Sharpe was immensely popular among ornithologists all over the world, and justly so, and was elected President of Section A at the Ornithological Congress held at Budapest in 1891 and at Paris in 1900: he was also elected President when the Congress met in London in 1905. He was an honorary LLD of the University of Aberdeen, a Fellow of the Linnean and Zoological Societies, a Member of the British Ornithologists' Union, an Honorary or Foreign Member of all the principal ornithological societies in the world, and a recipient of the Gold Medal for Science bestowed in 1891 by HIM the Emperor of Austria. Strange as it may seem, he was never elected a Fellow of the Royal Society, though his claims to that distinction seemed obvious enough, for services such as he rendered to science have rarely been achieved by one man in his lifetime. Scientific men in general are apt to belittle the work of the systematic zoologist, but they forget that without his help they would be unable to obtain a correct determination of any animal and might thus fall into serious errors. I could mention instances in which the elaborate work contained in certain anatomical memoirs has been rendered useless by the fact that the author was mistaken as to the species with which he was dealing.

Dr Sharpe was a well-known and most popular member of the Savage Club, and at one time was a regular attendant at the dinners given every Saturday night. One of the best evenings the writer remembers attending as a guest of that Club was on an occasion when Dr Sharpe was in the Chair.

Few people knew Dr Sharpe so well as the writer, who had been his colleague in the Natural History Museum for nearly twenty-eight years and co-operated with him in building up the now unrivalled collection of birds. Those who only met Dr Sharpe during the last ten years of his life cannot realize the extraordinary energy he formerly possessed and the enormous amount of work he was able to undertake and successfully accomplish. His immense and almost boyish enthusiasm never failed him to the end; but during the last few years of his life one could not help noticing with sorrow that his health was beginning to fail, and that the strain of many years of unremitting labour at high pressure had at last worn him out. Kind-hearted almost to a fault, his unfailing courtesy, good temper, and readiness to assist all those who sought information and help endeared him to everyone both at home and abroad. The cares of life, which in his case were many, and the deceitfulness of riches, which were few, hardly affected his exuberant spirits, and he was always cheery and full of good-natured chaff. His generosity was such that he was always ready to offer pecuniary assistance in any case of trouble that came under his notice, and it was therefore not surprising that he was frequently imposed upon.

It is sad to think that, after thirty-eight years of the most faithful and unselfish service to the nation, Dr Sharpe should not have been spared for a few years to enjoy his thoroughly well-earned pension. As it is, his wife and children are left very insufficiently provided for, and it is greatly to be hoped that some special means may be found of obtaining a pension for the family of so valuable a public servant.

W.R. OGILVIE-GRANT

P.L. Sclater

From the report on the Club's meeting on 11 June 1913.

The Hon. Walter Rothschild said that it was with great regret he had to intimate to the Members of the Club that their Chairman, Dr P.L. Sclater, had met with an accident and would be unable to join them on that occasion. This was the more to be regretted, as the occasion was a very special one, being the 21st anniversary of the Club. During all those years Dr Sclater had been an unfailing supporter of the Club and had seldom missed a meeting, and the Members had determined to mark the present occasion by presenting him with a testimonial and a piece of plate in commemoration of his long and faithful services.

Mr Rothschild said that the honour and pleasure of presenting these souvenirs had fallen on him, and that the absence of Dr Sclater would be as great a disappointment to all the Members as it was to himself. In the absence of his father, Mr W.L. Sclater had kindly consented to receive the gifts.

The testimonial, which took the form of a beautifully bound book, contained the following short address engrossed in coloured letters on vellum, and signed by nearly all the Members of the Club:

IN COMMEMORATION
OF THE
TWENTY-FIRST ANNIVERSARY
OF THE
BRITISH ORNITHOLOGISTS' CLUB.
FOUNDED IN OCTOBER, 1892

We, the undersigned Members of the British Ornithologists' Club, in presenting this testimonial to Philip Lutley Sclater, M.A., D.Sc., F.R.S., desire to record our high appreciation of his valuable services as Chairman during the past twenty-one years.

We would also express our admiration for the way in which he has at all times furthered the best interests of the Club by his untiring devotion, and we feel that the high status it has attained is largely due to his unfailing support.

The piece of plate, intended as a centre-piece for a dining-table, was in the form of a silver Ibis standing on a silver globe and mounted on an ebony stand bearing a tablet and inscription. The Ibis was a copy of the familiar drawing which ornaments the cover of *The Ibis*, the well-known journal of the British Ornithologists' Union, with which Dr Sclater had always been so closely connected as Editor. The globe had the land-areas of frosted silver and the seas of polished silver. This unique design, about fifteen inches in height, together with the testimonial, were handed to Mr W.L. Sclater, who in a few well-chosen words thanked the Members very sincerely for the beautiful gifts which he had received on behalf of his father. He deplored his father's absence, and explained that Dr Sclater had recently met with a carriage-accident and was still confined to his bed.* He felt sure, however,

*He died soon after, on 27 June 1913.

190

that if anything could accelerate his recovery it would be the kind thoughts of the Members of the Club in which he had always been so deeply interested.

Mr Rothschild said it was also his privilege on that memorable night to extend the warm welcome of the Club to Mr A.F.R. Wollaston and Mr C. Boden Kloss, who had just returned from their most successful ascent of Carstensz Peak, in the Snow Range of New Guinea. It was a great pleasure to see them back safe and sound, and apparently none the worse, after all the hardships they had endured. As they were there to tell their own story, it only remained for him to present to Mr Wollaston the Silver Medal of the BOU, which had been awarded to him after the previous attempt to reach the Snow Mountains by way of the Mimika River.

The late Philip Lutley Sclater

From the Bulletin *published on 24 October 1913.*

By the death of Philip Lutley Sclater, MA, DSc, FRS, a distinguished figure has been lost to science, and the British Ornithologists' Club has lost its Chairman. This office he had held since the formation of the Club in 1892. Sclater was born at Tangier Park, Hampshire, in November 1829, and he was educated at Winchester and Corpus Christi College, Oxford, where he graduated in 1849, and was subsequently elected a Fellow of his College. He was called to the Bar in 1855 and went on the Western Circuit for several years. In 1859 Sclater was elected Secretary of the Zoological Society, to which the greater part of his life's work was dedicated. During the forty-three years that he held that post, the Society gained immensely in numbers and prosperity, and the collection of animals in the gardens at Regent's Park became the most complete in the world.

Of the vast mass of work dealing with a great variety of different subjects, which Sclater dealt with during his long life, it is not very easy to say which is the most important, but it is probable that his work on zoogeography and the classification of birds will be longest remembered. In 1858 he published his essay on the six geographical regions, and in 1899 he elaborated on the subject in conjunction with his son, W.L. Sclater.

But it is with his work in connection with ornithology that this short notice must mainly deal. In 1856, 1857, and 1858 Sclater attended the annual conferences on birds with Newton, Tristram, Gurney, and others, and when in the latter year the British Ornithologists' Union was formed he was elected one of the twenty original members, and was appointed the first editor of *The Ibis*. With the exception of the second and third series, 1865 to 1876, Sclater's name appears, either alone or in conjunction with Salvin, Howard Saunders, and A.H. Evans, as editor of every volume of *The Ibis* until the end of 1912, when he relinquished the task.

His keen interest in geography and travel led to his being a constant attendant at meetings of the Royal Geographical Society, where he served on the Council, and was instrumental in turning the thoughts of many travellers to zoology as well as exploration.

One of the outstanding features throughout his career was the great interest he took in young students of ornithology and the help which he always gave in guiding them in their studies. His uniform kindness to foreign ornithologists made his name revered throughout the world, for he spared no trouble or fatigue in helping them to accomplish their wishes when visiting England. His great pleasure was to know that he had assisted them to carry out their scientific objects and rendered their stay either in England or in the colonies more pleasant and profitable. His hospitality to ornithologists in general, and to foreigners in particular, was inexhaustible and spontaneous.

Not a few members of this Club will remember with gratitude the advice and encouragement he gave them on setting forth on their travels, and the genuine interest with which he heard of their doings in different parts of the world. As Chairman of the British Ornithologists' Club he was very regular in his attendance at its meetings, and his inaugural address at the beginning of each session, when he gave an account of the doings of himself and of other ornithologists, was always listened to with interest by his 'brother Ibises'.

When the Club celebrated its twenty-first anniversary in June last, it was hoped that he would be present to receive an address from the members, and a present of a silver Ibis in grateful recognition of his long and valued services to the Club. Mr W.L. Sclater, in acknowledging the address, informed the meeting that his father was unfortunately ill as the result of a carriage accident, and it was with real sorrow that we learnt a few days later that he had died on June 27th. Sclater's grim and rugged face and his penetrating cry of 'Order, Order' will long remain in our memories.

Appendix

Currently accepted equivalents of obsolete specific names used in passages from the *Bulletin* quoted in the preceding pages

Alcyone lessoni = Ceyx azureus
Alcyone pusilla = Ceyx pusillus
Aprosmictus wilhelminae = Alisterus chloropterus

Baza jerdoni = Aviceda jerdoni

Cacatua triton = C. galerita
Calodromas elegans = Eudromia elegans
Calornis metallica = Aplonis metallica
Calophasis = Syrmaticus
Casuarius sclateri = C. casuarius
Ceyx solitarius = C. lepidus
Charmosyna stellata = C. papou
Charmosynopsis multistriata = Charmosyna multistriata
Charmosynopsis pulchella = Charmosyna pulchella
Chrysophlegma flavinucha = Picus flavinucha
Cinclus cashmeriensis = C. cinclus
Cyclopsittacus goodmani = Opopsitta gulielmitertii

Dacelo intermedia = D. leachii
Dasyptilus pesqueti = Psittrichas fulgidus
Dichoceros bicornis = Buceros bicornis

Eos furcata = Pseudeos furcata

Gallinago aequatorialis (not identified)
Gallinago australis (not identified)
Gallinago major = G. media
Gennaeus = Lophura
Goura sclateri = G. scheepmakeri

Homochlamys major = Cettia major

193

Horeites brunnifrons = Cettia brunnifrons
Huhua nipalensis = Bubo nipalensis

Ianthia hyperythra = Erithacus hyperythrus
Ianthia indica = Erithacus indicus

Lampromorpha caprius = Chrysococcyx caprius
Lanius major = L. excubitor
Linota linaria = Acanthis flammea
Loria mariae = L. loriae
Lorius erythrothorax = L. lory

Machlolophus spilonotus = Parus spilonotus
Megacrex ineptus = Amaurornis ineptus
Melanocorypha sibirica = M. leucoptera
Melanopyrrhus robertsoni = Mino anais
Microglossa aterrima = Probosciger aterrimus
Munia tristissima = Lonchura tristissima
Myristicivora spilorrhoa = Ducula spilorrhoa

Nitidula hodgsoni = Niltava hodgsoni

Oenanthe stapazina = O. hispanica

Pachyglossa melanozanthus = Coccothraustes melanozanthus
Parotia meeki = P. carolae
Perissospiza carnipes = Coccothraustes carnipes
Phyllergates coronatus = Orthotomus coronatus
Pipra opalizans = P. iris
Procarduelis rubescens = Carpodacus rubescens
Propyrrhula subhimachala = Pinicola subhimachala
Pterocles arenaria = P. orientalis
Ptilorhis intercedens = P. magnificus

Ruticilla titys = Phoenicurus ochruros

Sauromarptis gaudichaudi = Dacelo gaudichaud
Seicercus cantator = Phylloscopus cantator
Sibia nipalensis = Alcippe nipalensis
Siphia strophiata = Ficedula strophiata
Suthora humii = S. poliotis

Todopsis bonapartei = T. cyanocephala
Troglodytes nipalensis = T. troglodytes

Xanthomelas ardens = Xanthomelus ardens
Xiphoramphus superciliaris = Xiphirhynchus superciliaris

Index

Persons

Authors of passages quoted are indicated by page numbers in **bold**; other mentions of the persons concerned are in ordinary type. Names of authors merely referred to in review papers are not indexed.

Alexander, Boyd 6, 10
Alexander, C.J. 126
Alexander, H.G. 126, **128–9**
Amadon, D. 88, **115–7**
Andersson, C.J. 10
Arnold, A. 47

Balston, R.Y. 184
Bannerman, D.A. **173–4**, 183
Beal, F.E.L. 184
Beehler, B.M. **18**, **60–1**
Belcher, Sir C. **76–7**
Benson, C.W. 3
Berlepsch, Fr. von 170
Berry, J. 47
Bidwell, E. 148
Bishop, K.D. 18
Blanford, W.T. 9
Bonhote, J.L. **39–40**, 155, **166**
Booth, H.B. 69
Boswall, J. **77–9**
Brabourne, Lord 183
Bridgeman, Hon. R.O.B. 184
Briggs, W. 185
Bristow, G. 135–7
Bunyard, P.F. 68, **69–72**, 83, **84**, 85–6, 165
Burton, P.J.K. 61
Butterfield, W.R. 134–5, 137
Buxton, Lord 168
Buxton, P.A. 73

Cawdor, Lord 158–61
Cave, F.O. 26–9
Chance, E.P. 81–3, 86
Chapin, J.P. **34–5**
Charlton, Capt. 184
Clancey, P.A. 88, **105–9**
Clay, T. 181
Crowley, J.C. 184

d'Arenberg, Prince E. 184
Demment, M. **77–9**
Digby Piggott, Sir T. 67
Dixon, H.E.O. 184
Dresser, H.E. 9, 186
Dyer, C.M. 183

Eagle Clarke, W. 42–3, 45–6
Elwes, H.J. 169
Evans, E. 8

Farquhar, Capt. 12
Feare, C.J. 130
Festa, E. 12
Finnis, G. **176–8**
Fisher, J. 179
Fitter, R.S.R. **138–47**
Flower, W.S. 88, 174
Forbes, Dr. 6, 10
Frith, C. and D. **13**

Gadow, H. 3

Goeldi, E. 11
Goodfellow, W. 12, **13–18**, 31, **57–60**
Gould, C. 68–9
Gould, J. 12
Grant, C.H.B. 88, 115
Gray, G.R. 186
Gurney, G. 174

Hall, B.P. 115, 181
Hargitt, E. 3
Harrison, J.G. 2–3, 131
Harrison, J.M. 2, 131, 134
Hartert, E. 3, 68, 88, **93–4**, 148, 153, 155, **170–1**
Hellmayr, C.E. 11
Hides, J.G. 33
Hume, A.O. 187
Hurcomb, Lord 179
Huxley, J. 88, 103

Ihering, H. von 11
Inglis, C. 83
Ingram, C. 37, 45
Ingram, Sir W. 38

Jackson, F.J. 10
Johnston, Sir H. 7, 10
Jourdain, F.C.R. 82, 86, 88, **94–5**, **153–4**, 163, 165, 168
Justice, J.R. 150

Kinnear, N.B. 47–8
Kloss, C.B. 20–1, 191
Knox, A.G. 120, 130, 134, 147–8

Lack, D. 65, 88, **95–104**
Lascelles, Hon. G. 171
La Touche, J.D. 9, 43–4
Lawrence, T.E. 177
Leach, E.P. 132
Legge, Hon. G. 183
Le Roi, O. 184
Longfield, C. 179
Löns, H. 184
Lorentz, Dr. 19, 21
Lovat, Lord 10
Lovegrove, R. **163–4**
Lowe, G.C. 134
Lowe, P.R. 35–6, **47–9**

Macdonald, J.D. **26–9**
Manson-Bahr, P. **61–5**

Marchant, S. 73, **74–6**
Maxwell, Sir H. 67
Mayr, E. 5
Meade-Waldo, E.G.B. **73–4**, **155–63**, 166, 171, **172**
Mearns, E.A. 184
Meiklejohn, K.J. 183
Meiklejohn, M.F.M. 149, **179–80**
Meinertzhagen, R. **44–7**, **72–3**, **133**, **147–9**, **175–6**
Menzbier, Prof. 9
Meyer, A.B. 10
Moore, Prof. P. 22
Moreau, R.E. **50–6**
Musselwhite, D.W. **85–6**

Nehrkorn, A. 184
Nelson, T.H. 184
Newton, A. 8
Niholson, E.M 127, 150, 179
Nicoll, M.J. 40, 134, 137

Oates, E.W. 9
Ogilvie-Grant, W.R. 3, 6, 10, 21, **31–2**, **36–7**, **119–20**, **129–30**, 160, **185–9**
Oldham, C. **121–5**
O'Malley, Mr 33
Oustalet, E. 10
Owen, D.E. **156–9**, 163

Paddock, J.H. 129–30
Payne-Gallwey, Sir R. 184
Peavot, H. 184
Penrose, F.G. 40
Phillips, E.C. 155
Phillips, Lort 6, 10
Pike, O.G. 86
Pitman, C.S.R. **174–5**, 181
Pleske, Dr. 9
Portal, K.M. 47–9
Pycraft, W. 62
Pye-Smith, G. 180

Quaritch, B. 186

Ramsay, E.P. 184
Ramsay, L.N.G. 183
Rattray, Col. 82
Reichenow, A. 10
Reiser, O. 9
Richardson, W.B. 1
Rickett, C.B. 9, 43–4

Ridgway, R. 11
Rothschild, N.C. 171
Rothschild, W. (Lord) 2, 10, 31–2, 87,
    125, 148, 152, 155, 171, **183–4**, 189-91
Rüppell, E. 10

Salomonsen, F. 176
Salter, J.H. 153, **154–5**, 158, 163
Salvadori, Count 3, 12
Salvin, O. **1**, 3, 8
Saunders, H. 3, **136–7**, 148, 155
Scharff, Dr. 37
Scholey, G.J. 85
Schweppenburg, G. von 184
Sclater, P.L. **1**, 2–3, **5–13**, 137, 170,
    189–92
Sclater, W.L. 190
Scott, Canon 184
Seebohm, H. 3, 9
Selous, F.C. 184–5
Serle, W. 181
Seth-Smith, D. 148
Sharpe, A. 7
Sharpe, R.B. 3, 10, 12–13, 135, 185–9
Shaw, G.E. 22
Shaw Mayer, F. **33**
Shelley, G.E. 3, 9–10
Simons, P.O. 12
Simson, E.L. 180
Smooker, G.D. 77
Southern, H.N. **109–10**
Spencer, R. 181
Stevens, H. **22–5**
Stonor, C.R. **32–4**, 47

Strickland, H. 6
Stuart Baker, E.C. **65–7**, **82–3**, 86–7,
    88–93, 169
Styan, F.W. 9

Thorpe, W.H. **86**
Ticehurst, C.B. **136**, **172–3**
Ticehurst, N.F. 40
Trimen, R. 184
Tristram, H.B. 8
Tucker, B.W. **110–4**, **132–4**

Upcher, H.M. 82, 171

Van de Water, Lt. 20
Vaughan, A.G. 156, **159–60**, 164

Wainwright, C.B. 180
Wallis, H.M. **151–2**
Warrand, H.M. 119–20
Whitehead, C.H.J. 183
Whitehead, J. 1, 7, 10
Wiglesworth, L.C. 10, 12
Winton, W.E. de 155
Witherby, H.F. 40, 47, 49, 82, 86, **126–8**
Wollaston, A.F.R. **19–21**, 191
Wood, Casey 174
Woosnam, R.B. 183
Wyllie, I. 81

Yealland, J.J. 3
Yeates, G.K. 180

Zedlitz, Count 184

Birds

The birds indexed are those that are the subject of substantial discussion. Those that are merely listed, or briefly referred to in passing, are not indexed.

Acanthis flammea 41–2
Actitis hypolencos 65–6
Afropavo congensis 34–6
Asio flammeus 67–8
Astrapia mayeri 32–4
Astrapia, Ribbon-tailed 32–4

Birds of paradise 17, 21, 57–61
Bird of Paradise, King of Saxony 12–13
Bullfinch 42

Calophasis (Syrmaticus) mikado 31–2
Chaffinch 106
Columba albitorques 77–9
Cuckoo 81–6
Cuculus canorus 81–6

Dryocopus martius 138–47

Egret 172–3
Erithacus rubecula 95–104, 107

Falco concolor 50–6
Falcon, Sooty 50–6
Fringilla coelebs 106

Gallinago spp. 61–4
Garrulus glandarius 47–9
Grebe, Black-necked 120–5
Grebe, Slavonian 119–20

Jay 47–9

Kite, Red 153–64

Lark, Black 136–7

Melanocorypha yeltoniensis 136–7
Milvus milvus 153–64

Owl, Short-eared 67–8

Parus ater 36–8
Parus montanus 125–30
Parus spp. 105–6
Peacock, Congo 34–6
Pheasant, Mikado 31–2
Philohela minor 63–4
Pigeon, White-collared 77–9
Podiceps auritus 119–20

Podiceps nigricollis 120–5
Pteridophora alberti 12–13
Pterocles spp. 73–6
Pyrrhula pyrrhula 42

Redpoll, Holböll's 42
Redpoll, Mealy 41–2
Reinarda squamata 76–7
Robin 95–104, 107

Sandgrouse 73–6
Sandpiper, Common 65–6
Scolopax rusticola 63–4
Snipe 61–4
Starling 130–4
Sturnus vulgaris 130–4
Swift, Fork-tailed Palm 76–7

Tichodroma muraria 135
Tit, Irish Coal 36–8
Tit, Willow 125–30
Troglodytes troglodytes 106–7

Wallcreeper 135
Woodcock 61–4
Woodpecker, Black 138–47
Wren 106–7